ESSENTIALS OF SAFETY

General Industry Training and Reference Guide

Volume I

Made with

Use this QR Code to see if you have
the most current edition
or visit www.regqr/bk/59810.html

6 88550 60379 9

MANCOMM®

315 West Fourth Street
Davenport, Iowa 52801
(563) 323-6245
1-800-MANCOMM
(6 2 6 - 2 6 6 6)
Fax: (563) 323-0804

Website: http://www.mancomm.com
E-mail: safetyinfo@mancomm.com

Library of Congress Control Number: 2013942249
ISBN: 1-59959-810-8
Updated through January 2017

Table of Contents

Prefix

Training Fundamentals

Purpose and Scope of the Essentials of Safety (EOS)

Purpose

> To train supervisors, safety officers, safety coordinators, and others on OSHA regulations and requirements

> To assist in the coordination of a company's policies and procedures with OSHA requirements and the implementation of those policies, procedures, and requirements

> To ensure the comprehension of the larger ramifications of daily tasks and the training of those who complete them

Scope

The EOS is designed for a broad purpose. It is not designed for a specific industry or SIC/NAICS code, but rather to address the tasks, hazards, and environments that OSHA requires most employers to address.

Editor's Insight

Learning Outcomes

Trainers that complete EOS training program should know:

> OSHA's expectations for most areas of responsibility, including:
>> hazard identification
>> worker protection
>> personal protective equipment
>> regulatory requirements
>> handling and reporting accidents and injuries
> the specific OSHA regulations involved with common operations
> how to find OSHA information, if necessary

How Does the EOS Training Program Work?

The training programs for general industry and construction are each divided into two volumes:

> Volume 1 covers the information necessary for entry-level workers. If Volume 1 is being used by an OSHA-authorized trainer to train employees, 10-hour training cards can be issued to trainees based on the information contained therein.

> Volume 2 covers the more in-depth information necessary for supervisors or workers with some safety responsibilities. If Volume 2 is being used by an OSHA-authorized trainer to train employees, 30-hour training cards can be issued to trainees based on the information contained therein.

Note: Only trainers authorized by OSHA can issue 10- and 30-hour training cards. For more information on becoming an OSHA-authorized trainer, see http://www.osha.gov/dte/outreach/authorized.html.

Each training module consists of the following parts:

> the text of the module itself

> the PowerPoint presentation that corresponds to the module, with screen captures of each PowerPoint slide plus the citation to the specific OSHA regulation being discussed running down the side of each training module page

> the Instructor Notes, which contain supplemental information for instructors to use and the answers to all quiz questions

> the Student Workbook, which contains the forms, classroom exercises, worksheets, etc. that are referenced in the training module text, plus quizzes for each training module, as applicable

The Benefits and Drawbacks of Training

Benefits

Training, by itself, is not a safety program. Training alone does not identify or eliminate hazardous conditions, nor does it provide workers with the equipment or staffing they need to do a job safety. A successful safety program will also include:

> management's total commitment to accident prevention, including a financial investment in safety;

> employee involvement in the safety program; and

> an ongoing effort to identify and eliminate hazardous conditions in the workplace.

An effective overall safety program:

> benefits an employer's bottom line by reducing costs due to absenteeism, turnover, lost time, and litigation;

> lowers workers' compensation premiums;

> improves employee health;

> improves the employer/employee relationship while helping to build trust; and

> helps to ensure compliance with OSHA regulations and avoid fines and citations.

Drawbacks

Some of the drawbacks to instituting a training program are obvious; others are not:

> An effective training program requires a lot of management resources, both money and time.

> Training is a constant process. It is not enough to mention an OSHA requirement once. Follow-up training and even retraining are required.

> Employees are not always "invested" in their own safety and must be made to understand the importance of training and following safe operating procedures.

> Training, alone, is not sufficient. Employers must also have an ongoing hazard assessment process with physical inspections to identify and eliminate work hazards.

> Safety requires a commitment from both management and employees to sometimes be inconvenienced in order to get work done safely.

Blue Gavel OSHA Training Guide, 15th Ed.

Blue Gavel OSHA Training Guide, 15th Ed.

Training Workers

Different groups of workers have different training needs. Workers can be divided into roughly three groups for general training purposes: new hires, experienced workers, and supervisors.

Training New Hires

Newly hired workers are a high-risk group when it comes to accidents and injuries. The Bureau of Labor Statistics (BLS) has found that 40% of injured workers have been on the job less than a year. The BLS went on to ask why this was so, and discovered that in many cases, the workers lacked critical information they needed in order to do their jobs safely. For example, in the study:

> 71% of workers who suffered head injuries had received no training regarding hard hats.

> 61% of worker who were injured while servicing equipment had not received information on lockout procedures.

> 27% of workers hurt while using scaffolds had received no information on safety requirements for scaffold installation.

> 20% of workers who were injured while operating power saws had not been trained to operate the equipment safely.

New hires are limited in obvious ways:

> You must assume that you are starting with a clean slate. You must assume that new hires have no prior training or that any training they have received may not be adequate.

> New hires will always need some amount of site-specific training. For example, even if a new employee has been operating a forklift for 30 years, he/she will still need training on operating a forklift at that particular location—they need to know, for example, that the forklift keys are left kept in the supervisor's desk to avoid unauthorized use, or that the loading dock has a blind corner.

> New hires may not be familiar with standard operating procedures, the hazards of the equipment with which they will be working, or whom to ask if they have a question.

New workers need to be aware of the hazards of their jobs, and how to protect themselves, before they ever begin working. Basic information you should consider including in your new employee orientation training includes:

> **Hazards Specific to the Job:** Each worker must know the specific hazards of his or her new job.

> **Fire and Emergency Procedures:** Each worker should know his/her responsibilities in an emergency.

> **Injury/Illness Reporting:** If they are injured or become ill due to an occupational exposure, workers need to know to whom they should report their injury/illness in order to receive prompt care.

> **Chemical Hazards:** Any chemical hazards require training under the Hazard Communication Standard.

> **Restricted Areas or Tasks:** Employees may be told what they are supposed to do, but sometimes they get into trouble when they're not told what they shouldn't do. If there are restricted areas within the worksite (e.g., radiation areas) or job tasks that can only be performed by specially trained workers (such as lockout/tagout), make sure workers know.

> **Personal Protective Equipment:** If employees need to wear personal protective equipment (PPE), they have to be trained to use and care for it correctly. They also need instruction on the limitations of PPE so that they don't get in over their heads.

> **Protective Measures:** Whatever protective measures exist in the workplace, such as machine guards, must be pointed out to workers so that they will not bypass or circumvent them.

Blue Gavel OSHA Training Guide, 15ᵗʰ Ed.

Training Experienced Workers

Sometimes, you will have to provide training to experienced workers. You may find yourself providing training to employees who are part of your existing workforce for one of the following reasons:

> A standard requires it. A number of OSHA training regulations specifically require that workers be retrained every year or during some other fixed period. For example, OSHA regulations require the following:

>> **Bloodborne Pathogens:** annual retraining

>> **Hazardous Chemical Emergency Response:** annual retraining

>> **Lockout/Tagout:** annual inspection to verify compliance

>> **Forklift Safety:** evaluation at least every three years

>> **Hazard Communication:** additional training whenever a new chemical hazard is introduced into the workplace

>> **Hearing Protection:** annual training for each worker in a hearing conservation program

>> **Respiratory Protection:** annual retraining

Blue Gavel OSHA Training Guide, 15th Ed.

» **Emergency Action:** retraining whenever the plan changes or the employee's responsibilities under the plan change

» **Fire Safety:** annual retraining on portable fire extinguishers provided for employee use; for fire brigade members, training "frequently enough" to ensure that each member is able to satisfactorily and safely perform assigned duties, but no less than annually; for fire brigade members who perform interior structural firefighting, at least quarterly retraining

» **Confined Spaces:** retraining as necessary to retain proficiency

› A new hazard has been introduced into the workplace.

› Safety procedures, equipment, technology, or work practices have changed.

› A worker has been promoted or reassigned.

› Employees are not working safely. Retraining should be performed if:

» near misses, accidents, or injuries increase,

» workers are observed committing unsafe acts, or

» any other reason makes a reminder seem in order.

Training Supervisors

Supervisors have a lot of responsibility when it comes to the safety of their workers, but they often don't receive the training they need to do this part of their jobs well. Be sure to provide it for them, as it can make a big difference. One study found that supervisors who were trained to properly respond, communicate, and problem solve with their workers about ergonomic problems had a substantial impact, as new disability claims dropped by 47% and lost-time claims by 18%. Make sure your supervisors understand their responsibilities for the following:

› **Training:** Supervisors may have to provide training themselves or just recognize when they need to schedule it. Make sure supervisors know what they're supposed to do, and make sure that they have the resources to get it done.

› **Responding to Accidents and Injuries:** When a worker is injured, his/her supervisor will probably be the first to know. So, the supervisor will have to know either how to initiate the appropriate workers' compensation paperwork and how to record the injury for OSHA, or the supervisor will have to know whom to contact to get those things done.

> **Hazard Identification:** If a supervisor knows about a hazard but fails to act, the employer is liable. Make sure your supervisors know how to identify workplace hazards and what they can do to eliminate those hazards.

> **Discipline:** Workers who violate safety procedures should be subject to disciplinary procedures, so supervisors should be familiar with both safety-related work rules and the discipline procedures that can be used to enforce them.

Training Employees Who Speak Another Language or Cannot Read

On April 28, 2010, OSHA issued a memorandum reiterating its training standards policy. According to the memo, it is OSHA's policy that "employee training required by OSHA standards must be presented in a manner than employees can understand." No matter the precise regulatory language, the terms "train," "instruct," and their synonyms require employers "to present information in a manner than employees receiving it are capable of understanding."

In practical terms, this means:

> Employers must instruct employees using both a language and a vocabulary that the employees can understand.

> Employers may have to provide safety training in languages other than English.

> If an employee's vocabulary is limited, then the safety training provided must account for that limitation.

> If employees cannot read, then telling them to read training materials will not satisfy the employer's training obligation.

> When a standard (such as the Lockout/Tagout Standard or the Forklift Standard) requires employers to assess employee comprehension, this must be done in a way that accommodates the employee's language skills.

Blue Gavel OSHA Training Guide, 15th Ed.

**Blue Gavel OSHA
Training Guide, 15th Ed.**

Training Older Workers

According to the BLS, employment of workers aged 65 and older increased by 101% from 1997 to 2007. By 2025, the proportion of workers over age 55 is expected to reach 20%. In addition, BLS data suggests that productivity increases when there is a higher percentage of workers over 55, while accident frequency in that age group shows a decline. In general, studies show that:

> Older workers exhibit lower job turnover and more dedication to the workplace.

> Older workers have more positive work values.

> Older workers are absent less frequently.

> Older workers often tend to be more accurate in their work.

> Older workers make more correct decisions than faster, younger co-workers.

> Older workers often have superior judgment, especially when it comes to safety.

> Older people are not any more likely to shun new technology than young people are.

When dealing with training an aging workforce, keep in mind the following tips:

> Because learning is based on previous experience, training for older workers may need to be more "practically" based.

> Tailor your training program to the age, knowledge, and experience of older workers to reduce feelings of frustration.

> The justification and logic behind the information being given—why you're doing what you're doing—are likely to be more important to older workers.

> Training, especially on tasks that depend on short-term memory, may take longer than with younger workers.

> Older workers may have a need for more assistance or practice.

> Older workers may find it hard to learn with complex or confusing stimuli, so ensure that your training sessions take place in a quiet place with few distractions.

> Because formal study habits decline with disuse, trainers may need to help older workers brush up on learning strategies. Consider distributing a list of simple study tips.

> If possible, provide training well in advance of when the new skills will be needed. While older workers are just as "trainable" as younger ones, evidence does suggest that they take longer to learn. However, once they do master a task, they tend to be more accurate than younger workers.

> Researchers believe that older workers will be more likely to assimilate and retain new materials if ideas are presented one at a time along with their practical application on the job.

> Because vision and hearing do decrease with age, ensure that any visuals used in training are big enough for everyone to see.

Training Documentation

OSHA generally requires employers to document their training efforts and, on request, to provide the agency with all materials used in any required training program. Specific training regulations usually require employers to keep training materials for at least the duration of a worker's employment, if not longer.

OSHA sometimes requires a "certification" to establish training of employees. A certification is written documentation verifying that the employee understand the training and can apply it in the workplace. Any training certification requirements for the training topics in this product are mentioned in the appropriate training module.

In addition to a list of attendees and their job titles, a complete record of training should also include:

> a copy of the instructor's credentials, if any;

> a brief outline of the subjects covered in the classroom; and

> a description of any practical experience provided.

Some OSHA standards explicitly require that these records be kept, and others don't make it mandatory. However, keeping these records will make it easy to demonstrate that training was conducted by a qualified individual and that it covered all OSHA-required and workplace-appropriate subject matter.

Effective Training

Effective training incorporates two important points:

> Most people have one learning style that's their preferred learning style—the method by which they learn most easily.

> Almost everyone masters a subject more quickly if all of the different types of learning styles are incorporated into the lesson plan.

Blue Gavel OSHA Training Guide, 15th Ed.

Learning Styles

Effective trainers will present the material in more than one way in order to encompass all learning styles so that trainees will be more likely to comprehend and retain it. An effective trainer will present materials in each of the following ways:

› **Visual:** Some people learn best when they can see the lesson. Visual learners may have strong verbal skills; in that case, giving them a handout may be the best way to convey information to them. Other visual learners may be strongly non-verbal; given a list of instructions, they may be confused, but given a picture or diagram, they'll understand. For this type of learner, incorporate illustrations into your presentation. For example:

  » Take pictures in the workplace and put them on handouts or slides.

  » Show videos that give a clear picture of safe vs. unsafe work practices.

  » Use diagrams and graphs to convey information, such as safety statistics, in a way that will have the greatest impact on this group.

› **Audible:** Some people remember best what they hear. This type of learner will get the most out of the lecture portion of a lesson. But, as with visual learners, don't limit yourself to words. For example:

  » Let trainees know what a piece of equipment sounds like when it's working properly.

  » Let employees hear workplace alarms.

  » Give employees a musical cue to help them remember important information.

› **Tactile:** Some people can't truly master something until they've done it, and others learn best when they're moving, rather than sitting still. Try to provide opportunities to practice skills. Also, try to get trainees moving during the training session. For example:

  » Bring actual equipment into the classroom and let trainees pass it around and examine it during class.

If you've presented a lesson in all of these ways, then you've not only presented the same lesson more than once, improving retention, but you've presented it in the way that each employee can most easily grasp, improving comprehension. Try to take learning styles into account when evaluating training, too. Some employees may do fine on a written evaluation; other may be better able to provide verbal explanation. Still others may be able to show you how to do a job safely even if they do poorly on written examinations.

The Characteristics of Effective Training

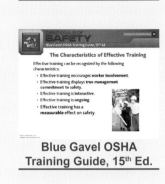

Blue Gavel OSHA Training Guide, 15th Ed.

Effective training can be recognized by the following characteristics:

> Effective training encourages **worker involvement**. Workers who participate materially in their training—for example, workers who wear respirators and who are required to put on, take off, and adjust their respirators during their training session—will get more out of their training than workers who are required to simply sit still and watch.

> Effective training displays **true management commitment to safety**. When management has made a tangible investment in safety, such as providing safer equipment and then training employees in its use, employees are more likely to commit to the safety program themselves.

> Effective training is **interactive**. Workers who are able to ask for clarification when they don't understand, or use their own experiences as examples of how the training is useful, achieve higher levels of comprehension than workers who have no one to ask when they're confused or who can't relate the training to what they do. **Note:** This EOS safety training program uses case studies, classroom discussions, and quizzes to make training interactive.

> Effective training is **ongoing**. Because repetition is essential to learning, and practice is essential to mastery, it's not enough to provide an initial training course and then leave workers on their own. "Toolbox meetings," or informal, on-the-job safety training sessions on a specific topic that last 10 to 15 minutes, are often incorporated into effective safety training programs to reinforce the fundamentals of a topic after the formal instruction.

> Effective training has a **measurable** effect on safety. Whether employees are evaluated immediately through testing, or over time through the assessment of accident rates, good training should show a measurable effect on safety.

**Blue Gavel OSHA
Training Guide, 15ᵗʰ Ed.**

Creating a Culture of Safety

"Culture" can be defined as the attitudes, feelings, values, and behaviors that characterize and inform society as a whole or any social group within it. A culture of safety in the workplace consists of an entire roster of employees and management who have a positive attitude about workplace safety, who feel safe, who value their own lives and the lives of those around them and who are valued by a company that is committed to keeping them safe, and who behave in a safe manner at all times. Creating a culture of safety within the workplace is not an easy task. Here are some tips for doing so:

> Encourage the reporting of hazards, unsafe acts, incidents, accidents, and near misses. Treat such reports as opportunities to create an even safer workplace. Handle all reports with concern rather than condemnation. **Note:** Section 11(c) of the OSH Act prohibits employers from discriminating against employees who exercise their rights under the OSHA Act. See Module 1, Introduction to OSHA, for more information.

> Make safety training persistent and pertinent by holding daily, short (5-minute) meetings on different safety topics that are pertinent to your industry or workplace. Use the time to address issues that have come up recently, to find out how much employees actually remember about a given topic, and to solicit feedback and information to determine how the training information being received is being used on the job.

> Record and publish training and injury/illness statistics.

> Consider the use of safety incentives. However, be very careful— do not institute an incentive program that discourages injury/illness reporting either intentionally or unintentionally. Programs that reward employees who have not reported injuries, or that reward teams of workers on which no one is injured over a period of time, may be perceived by OSHA as discriminatory toward workers who do report injuries. OSHA maintains that these types of programs violate Section 11(c) of the OSH Act, which prohibits employers from discriminating in any manner against employees who exercise a protected right, including the right to report a workplace injury.

Module One

Introduction to OSHA

Lesson Overview

Purpose:

› To provide workers with introductory information about OSHA

Topics:

1. Why is OSHA important to you?

2. What rights do you have under OSHA?

3. What responsibilities does your employer have under OSHA?

4. What do the OSHA standards say?

5. How are OSHA inspections conducted?

6. Where can you go for help?

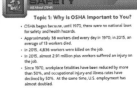

Topic 1: Why Is OSHA Important to You?

› OSHA began because, until 1970, there were no national laws for safety and health hazards.

› Approximately 38 workers died every day in 1970; in 2015, an average of 13 workers died.

› In 2015, 4,836 workers were killed on the job.

› In 2015, almost 2.91 million plus workers suffered an injury on the job.

› **Since 1970, workplace fatalities have been reduced by more than 50%, and occupational injury and illness rates have declined by 50%. At the same time, U.S. employment has almost doubled.**

Discussion Questions

› When, during your work experience, did you first hear about OSHA?

› What did you think about OSHA then?

› What do you think OSHA's job is?

Group Activity: Worker Fatalities Reported

Handout: "Worker Fatalities Reported to OSHA" in Student Workbook

› Each group reviews the handout and selects an incident to discuss.

› Have full class share what they discussed in the groups.

History of OSHA

› OSHA stands for the Occupational Safety and Health Administration, an agency of the U.S. Department of Labor.

› OSHA's responsibility is worker safety and health protection.

› On December 29, 1970, President Nixon signed the OSH Act.

› This Act created OSHA, the agency, which formally came into being on April 28, 1971.

Who Does OSHA Cover?

Nearly every American employee is covered by OSHA (or an OSHA-approved state agency). The significant exceptions are:

› self-employed individuals;

› immediate family members of farm employers that do not employ outside employees;

› employees whose safety and health is covered by any state or federal agency other than OSHA (e.g., the Mine Safety and Health Administration, the Federal Aviation Administration, the military); and

› public employees in state and local governments that are not in a state with an OSHA-approved program.

OSHA Coverage Activity

Covered by OSHA?		Worker
YES	NO	1. Harry Adams, a miner at Below Ground Inc.
YES	NO	2. Adrian Smith, one of 3 employees of ABC Landscaping.
YES	NO	3. Taylor Dell, an accountant in business for herself.
YES	NO	4. Rob Jones, one of 10 carpenters working for Woody, Inc.

OSHA's Mission

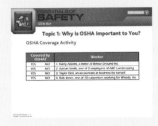

> The mission of OSHA is to save lives, prevent injuries, and protect the health of America's workers.

> Some of the things OSHA does to carry out its mission are:

>> developing job safety and health standards and enforcing them through worksite inspections;

>> maintaining a reporting and recordkeeping system to keep track of job-related injuries and illnesses; and

>> providing training programs to increase knowledge about occupational safety and health.

State Plans

Federal OSHA's rules generally preempt (supersede or replace) state safety laws. However, the OSHA Act allows states to administer their own safety and health plans by obtaining approval from federal OSHA. Twenty-one states, plus Puerto Rico, have done so with respect to private employers. Another five states, plus the Virgin Islands, administer their own safety and health plans for public employers.

STATUS OF STATE OCCUPATIONAL SAFETY AND HEALTH PLANS

FEDERAL PLAN STATES

STATE PLAN STATES

STATE PLAN STATES FOR STATE & LOCAL GOVERNMENT EMPLOYEES ONLY

> To obtain federal OSHA's approval, a state must adopt safety regulations that are comparable to federal OSHA's. The standards need not be identical, as long as they are at least as effective.

> Once federal OSHA approves a state plan, the state occupational safety and health agency has primary authority for enforcing occupational safety and health laws in that state. The state agency investigates complaints and conducts inspections in place of federal OSHA.

> States must modify their own standards to keep current with federal changes; whenever federal OSHA adopts a new standard, states have six months to adopt a comparable standard.

> Some examples of state plan differences include stricter permissible exposure limits to certain chemicals than federal OSHA, additional safety program requirements (e.g., some states require employers to have an Injury and Illness Prevention Plan), and additional safety duties (e.g., Oregon requires employers to either establish a safety committee or hold safety meetings with their employees).

Questions for Review

> Why was OSHA necessary?

> What is OSHA's mission?

> Why is this training important?

Topic 2: What Rights Do You Have Under OSHA?

> You have the right to the following:

>> a safe and healthful workplace

>> know about hazardous chemicals

>> information about injuries and illnesses in your workplace

>> complain or request hazard correction from employer

>> training

>> know the hazards to which you will be exposed

>> medical records

>> file a complaint with OSHA

>> participate in an OSHA inspection

>> be free from retaliation for exercising safety and health rights

>> refuse, under certain conditions, to work in a situation in which you would be exposed to hazards

Worker Rights

Handout: OSHA Poster

> Have you seen this poster at your place of work?

> Which of the employee rights listed on the poster do you think is the most important?

Discussion

Your Right to... A Safe and Healthful Workplace

> The creation of OSHA provided workers the right to a safe and healthful workplace.

> Section 5(a)(1) of the OSH Act states: "Each employer shall furnish to each of his employees employment and a place of employment which are free from recognized hazards that are causing or are likely to cause death or serious physical harm to his employees." This is known as the "General Duty Clause."

OSHA Act of 1970, Section 5(a)

Your Right to... Know About Hazardous Chemicals

> Employers must have a written, complete hazard communication program that includes information on:

>> container labeling,

>> safety data sheets (SDSs), and

>> worker training, which must include the physical and health hazards of the chemicals and how workers can protect themselves including specific procedures the employer has implemented to protect workers, such as work practices, emergency procedures, and personal protective equipment.

§1900.1200

Discussion

§1904

§1977.9(c)

§1910.9(b)

Classroom Exercise: SDSs

Handout: SDS Example

> What information does the SDS provide?

> Has anyone seen an SDS in their workplace?

> Were the instructions on the SDS followed in their workplace?

> Has anyone worked with hazardous substances without SDSs?

Your Right to... Injury & Illness Information

> OSHA's Recordkeeping Rule requires most employers with more than 10 workers to keep a log of injuries and illnesses.

> Workers have the right to review the current log, as well as the logs stored for the past five years.

> Workers also have the right to view the annually posted summary of the injuries and illnesses (OSHA 300A).

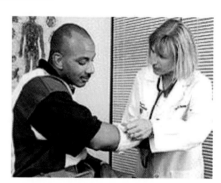

Your Right to... Complain or Request Corrections

> Workers may bring up safety and health concerns in the workplace to their employers without fear of discharge or discrimination, as long as the complaint is made in good faith.

> OSHA regulations [29 CFR 1977.9(c)] protect workers who complain to their employer about unsafe or unhealthful conditions in the workplace.

Your Right to... Training

> Workers have a right to get training from employers on a variety of health and safety hazards and standards that employers must follow.

> Some required training covers topics such as lockout/tagout, bloodborne pathogens, noise, confined spaces, fall hazards in construction, and personal protective equipment, along with a variety of other subjects.

Your Right to... Examine Exposure & Medical Records

> Employees and former employees who are exposed to toxic substances or harmful physical agents in the workplace have the right to access their medical and exposure records.

> Examples of toxic substances and harmful physical agents include:

>> metals and dusts, such as lead, cadmium, and silica

>> biological agents, such as bacteria, viruses, and fungi

>> physical stress, such as noise, heat, cold, vibration, repetitive motion, and ionizing and non-ionizing radiation

§1910.1020

Your Right to... File a Complaint with OSHA

> Workers may file a complaint with OSHA if they believe a violation of a safety or health standard, or an imminent danger situation, exists in the workplace.

> Workers may request that their names not be revealed to the employer.

> If a worker files a complaint, they have the right to find out OSHA's action on the complaint and request a review if an inspection is not made.

> To file a complaint:

>> Download the OSHA-7 form from OSHA's website.

>> File the complaint online, by fax or mail, or by telephone.

>> You can also telephone or visit local, regional, or area offices to discuss your concerns.

>> Complete the form—be specific and include appropriate details.

>> OSHA determines if an inspection is necessary.

>> Workers do not have to reveal their names.

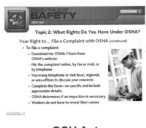

OSH Act

Topic 2: What Rights Do You Have Under OSHA?

Group Activity: Filing an OSHA Complaint

See the "Filing an OSHA Complaint" handout in the Student Workbook.

• Each group reviews the handout and discusses the complaint scenario.
• Groups need to determine what information would be important to include in their complaint.
• Have the class discuss the group's results:
  – What was included in the complaint?
  – What was added to the complaint?

Discussion

Topic 2: What Rights Do You Have Under OSHA?

Your Right to... Participate in an OSHA Inspection

• An employee representative can accompany OSHA inspector.
• Workers can talk to the inspector privately.

§1903.10

Topic 2: What Rights Do You Have Under OSHA?

Your Right to... Participate in an OSHA Inspection (continued)

• Workers may point out hazards, describe injuries, illnesses, or near misses that resulted from those hazards, and describe any concern they have about a safety or health issue.
• Workers can find out about inspection results and abatement measures and may object to dates set for violations to be corrected.

Section 11(c) of OSH Act

Topic 2: What Rights Do You Have Under OSHA?

Your Right to... Be Free from Retaliation

• Workers have the right to be free from retaliation for exercising safety and health rights.
• Workers have a right to seek safety and health on the job without fear of punishment.
• This right is spelled out in Section 11(c) of the OSH Act.
• Workers have 30 days to contact OSHA and file a complaint if they feel they have been punished for exercising their safety and health rights.

Group Activity: Filing an OSHA Complaint

Handout: Filing an OSHA Complaint

› Each group reviews the handout and discusses the industry-specific scenario.

› Groups need to determine what information would be important to include in their complaint.

› Have the class discuss the group's results:

  » What was included in the complaint?

  » What was added to the complaint?

Your Right to... Participate in an OSHA Inspection

› An employee representative can accompany OSHA inspector.

› Workers can talk to the inspector privately.

› Workers may point out hazards, describe injuries, illnesses, or near misses that resulted from those hazards, and describe any concern they have about a safety or health issue.

› Workers can find out about inspection results and abatement measures and may object to dates set for violations to be corrected.

Your Right to... Be Free from Retaliation

Refer to the "Your Rights as a Whistleblower" handout in your Student Workbook.

› Workers have the right to be free from retaliation for exercising safety and health rights.

› Workers have a right to seek safety and health on the job without fear of punishment.

› This right is spelled out in Section 11(c) of the OSH Act.

› Workers have 30 days to contact OSHA and file a complaint if they feel they have been punished for exercising their safety and health rights.

Your Right to... Refuse to Work

› You have a legal right to refuse to work in a situation where all of the following are true:

» You have asked your employer to eliminate a danger, and the employer failed to do so.

» You refuse to work in "good faith," meaning you must genuinely believe that an imminent danger exists.

» A reasonable person would agree that there is a real danger of death or serious injury.

» There isn't enough time, due to the urgency of the hazard, to get it corrected through regular enforcement channels, such as requesting an OSHA inspection.

› According to OSHA, you should take all of the following steps:

» Ask your employer to correct the hazard or to assign other work.

» Tell your employer that you won't perform the work unless and until the hazard is corrected.

» Remain at the worksite until ordered to leave by your employer.

§1977.12

Discussion

Classroom Exercise: Refusal to Work

Handout: Refusing to Work Because Conditions Are Dangerous

› Has anyone encountered working conditions that made you afraid to work because of dangerous conditions?

› How did you handle the problem?

Questions for Review

› What does an SDS tell you?

› What are some worker rights related to injury and illness reporting?

› Name some standards or hazards where worker training is required.

› Under what conditions can you legally refuse to work?

OSHA Regulations

Section 5(a) of the OSH Act; §1904

Topic 3: What Responsibilities Does Your Employer Have Under OSHA?

⟩ Provide a workplace free from recognized hazards and comply with OSHA standards.

⟩ Provide training required by OSHA standards.

⟩ Keep records of injuries and illnesses.

⟩ Provide medical exams when required by OSHA standards and provide workers access to their exposure and medical records.

⟩ Not discriminate against workers who exercise their rights under the Act (Section 11(c)).

⟩ Post OSHA poster, citations, and abatement verification notices.

⟩ Provide and pay for personal protective equipment (PPE) and adhere to their requirements.

Employers Are Required to:

Provide a Workplace Free from Recognized Hazards

Refer to the "Identifying Safety and Health Problems in the Workplace" handout in the Student Workbook.

Keep Records of Injuries and Illnesses

	Reporting and Recording Checklist
Employers must:	
✓	Report all work-related fatalaties within 8 hours
✓	Report all work-related, in-patient hospitalizations within 24 hours
✓	Report all work-related amputations or losses of an eye within 24 hours
✓	Maintain injury and illness records
✓	Inform workers how to report an injury or illness to the employer
✓	Make records available to workers
✓	Allow OSHA access to records
✓	Post annual summary of injuries and illnesses

Classroom Exercise: OSHA 300

Handout: OSHA 300 Log Example

> How many workers reported injuries or illnesses?

> What types of injuries and illnesses were reported?

> What jobs and departments had the most severe injuries or illnesses?

Employers Are Required to:

Provide and Pay for Personal Protective Equipment

Refer to the "Employers Must Provide and Pay for PPE" handout in the Student Workbook.

> Employers are required to determine if personal protective equipment (PPE) should be used to protect their workers.

> When PPE is required, it must be provided and paid for by the employer.

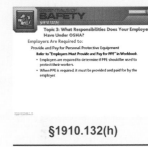

§1910.132(h)

Questions for Review

> What are some of the responsibilities employers have related to OSHA recordkeeping?

> Which section of the OSH Act prohibits employers from discriminating against workers for exercising their safety and health rights?

> What are some types of PPE that employers must pay for?

Discussion

Topic 4: What Do the OSHA Standards Say?

> OSHA standards fall into four categories: General Industry, Construction, Maritime, and Agriculture.

> OSHA issues standards for a wide variety of workplace hazards.

> Where there are no specific OSHA standards, employers must comply with the General Duty Clause, Section 5(a)(1).

OSHA Regulations

Most Frequently Cited Standards

Editor's Insight

On the OSHA website at http://www.osha.gov/oshstats/index.html, click "Frequently Cited OSHA Standards" to view current data.

To search data on this webpage:

> "Select number of employees in establishment," select ALL or one of the options listed.

> "Federal or State Jurisdiction," select Federal or, from the dropdown menu, a specific state.

> "NAICS," leave blank for a list of industry groups. The 2- or 3-digit codes can be used for industry sectors or sub-sectors.

Discussion

Classroom Exercise: OSHA Standards

Handout: Standards: 29 CFR 1910 – General Industry

> What is the Subpart for Personal Protective Equipment?

> What is the Subpart for Machinery and Machine Guarding?

> What topic does 1910, Subpart H, cover?

§1903.6; §1903.7

Topic 5: How Are OSHA Inspections Conducted?

> The OSH Act authorizes OSHA compliance safety and health officers (CSHOs) to conduct workplace inspections at reasonable times.

> OSHA conducts inspections without advance notice, except in rare circumstances (e.g., imminent danger).

>> In fact, anyone who tells an employer about an OSHA inspection in advance can receive fines and a jail term.

OSHA Inspection Priority

Priority	Category of Inspection
1st	**Imminent Danger:** Reasonable certainty an immediate danger exists
2nd	**Fatality/Catastrophe:** Reported to OSHA; inspected ASAP
3rd	**Complaints/Referrals:** Workers, worker representatives, or others can file a complaint about a safety or health hazard
4th	**Programmed Inspections:** Cover industries and employers with high injury and illness rates, specific hazards, or other exposures.

Citations and Penalties

Violation Type	Penalty
Willful A violation that the employer intentionally and knowingly commits or a violation that the employer commits with plain indifference to the law.	OSHA may propose penalties of up to $124,709 for each willful violation, with a minimum penalty of $8,908 for each willful violation.
Serious A violation where there is substantial probability that death or serious physical harm could result and the employer knew, or should have known, of the hazard.	There is a mandatory penalty for serious violations which may be up to $12,471.
Other-Than-Serious A violation that has a direct relationship to safety and health, but probably would not cause death or serious physical harm.	OSHA may propose a penalty of up to $12,471 for each other-than-serious violation.
Repeated A violation that is the same or similar to a previous violation.	OSHA may propose penalties of up to $124,709 for each repeated violation.

OSHA Field Operations Manual

Discussion

Questions for Review

> Give an example of a reason why OSHA would conduct an inspection at your workplace.

> What are some of the types of OSHA violations?

Editor's Insight

Topic 6: Where Can You Go For Help?

› Sources within the workplace/worksite

› Sources outside the workplace/worksite

Sources Within the Workplace/Worksite

› employer or supervisor, co-workers, and union representatives

› safety data sheet (SDS) for information on chemicals

› labels and warning signs

› employee orientation manuals or other training materials

› work tasks and procedures instruction

Sources Outside the Workplace/ Worksite

See the "Safety & Health Resources" and the "Navigating the OSHA Website" handouts from your Student Workbook.

› OSHA website (http://www.osha.gov) and OSHA offices (You can call or write.)

› Compliance Assistance Specialists in the OSHA area offices

› National Institute for Occupational Safety and Health (NIOSH)–OSHA's sister agency

› OSHA Training Institute Education Centers

› doctors, nurses, other health care providers

› public libraries

› other local, community-based resources

Questions for Review

> What are some resources inside the workplace that will help you find information on safety and health issues?

> What are some resources outside the workplace that will help you find information on safety and health issues?

Session Summary

OSHA®

This lesson covered:

> the importance of OSHA, including the history of safety and health regulation leading to the creation of OSHA and OSHA's mission;

> worker rights under OSHA;

> employer responsibilities;

> OSHA standards;

> OSHA inspections; and

> safety and health resources, including how to file a complaint.

Discussion

Notes

Module Two

RegLogic™

Title 29 CFR 1910

"CFR" stands for "Code of Federal Regulations."

› Title 29 is for Labor.

» Part 1903 contains regulations for inspections, citations, and proposed penalties.

» Part 1904 contains regulations for recording and reporting occupational injuries and illnesses.

» Part 1910 contains occupational safety and health standards for general industry.

  › 1910 is broken into Subparts A through Z and sections 1910.1 through 1910.1450.

  › Sections are formatted in an outline with paragraphs and subparagraphs.

» Parts 1915, 1917, and 1918 contain maritime regulations.

» Part 1926 contains safety and health regulations for construction.

» Part 1928 contains occupational safety and health standards for agriculture.

» There are two types of appendices, which are either mandatory or non-mandatory:

  › Subpart Appendices

  › Section Appendices

Code of Federal Regulations

Editor's Insight

Discussion

RegLogic™

At a minimum, what must be covered in training employees for bloodborne pathogens?

› Look up bloodborne pathogens in the index and find the page number. (Use the actual page number found in your index.)

› Go to the page number listed under bloodborne pathogens and find the centered header highlighted in RED for the standard number.

› Do your ABC's! Search all the red paragraph headings before deciding the following question….

Which is most relevant to training?

› So far, we have §1910.1030(g). Search the next level, it starts with number (1).

› Once again, which is most relevant to training?

› Now, we are at §1910.1030(g)(2). Search the next level it starts with Roman numeral (i).

Where are the minimum requirements for bloodborne pathogens training?

The answer is:

Section 1910.1030

Paragraph (g)

Subparagraph (2)

Roman numeral (vii)

And looks like this: §1910.1030(g)(2)(vii)

Hazard Violation Search Workshop

Handout: Hazard Violation Search Workshop

› Using the RegLogic index in the CFR, find the regulations for the following workplace hazards.

› Write the standard number down on the right side of the form.

regSMART™

Throughout the Essentials of Safety Training Management System, you will find tables labeled "regSMART™" at the beginning of each module. regSMART™ acts as a practical organizational tool as it breaks down the regulations concerning each module into the following categories:

> **S**cope: Application

> **M**anagement Controls: Engineering controls, administrative controls, and personal protective equipment

> **A**lerts: Postings, signs, tags, markings, and labels

> **R**ecords: Written programs, training records, medical records, and inspection records

> **T**raining: Employee training requirements

regSMART™ is especially helpful to users as OSHA does not follow a distinct pattern in the way it presents information. For instance, training requirements for Bloodborne Pathogens are located in paragraph (g)(2), whereas training requirements for Emergency Response to Hazardous Substance Releases are found in paragraphs (q)(5) – (8) and (11).

In addition, not all regulations are applicable to every employee, making regSMART™ a useful device for quick reference. For extra clarification, let's see how regSMART™ deals with "Control of Hazardous Energy (Lockout/Tagout)."

Editor's Insight

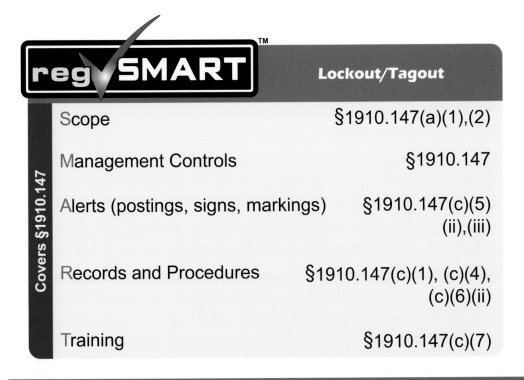

reg✓SMART™	Lockout/Tagout
Scope	§1910.147(a)(1),(2)
Management Controls	§1910.147
Alerts (postings, signs, markings)	§1910.147(c)(5) (ii),(iii)
Records and Procedures	§1910.147(c)(1), (c)(4), (c)(6)(ii)
Training	§1910.147(c)(7)

Covers §1910.147

Editor's Insight

In this case:

› The **S**cope of the regulation is located in 1910.147(a)(1) and (2) and pertains to the control of energy during the service and maintenance of machines and equipment.

› **M**anagement Controls, found in 1910.147, refer to the establishment and enforcement of a lockout/tagout program.

› **A**lerts (1910.147(c)(5)(ii) and (iii)), describe the requirements for lockout/tagout devices including durability, substantiality, and labeling.

› Regulations concerning **R**ecords are found in 1910.147(c)(1), (c)(4), and (c)(6)(ii), and involve the documentation of lockout/tagout programs and procedures.

› **T**raining (1910.147(c)(7)), as you may guess, discusses the requirements for training and retraining employees.

Therefore, besides being an invaluable means for quick reference, regSMART™ also becomes a beneficial tool for further exploration into the regulations.

Module Three
Walking-Working Surfaces

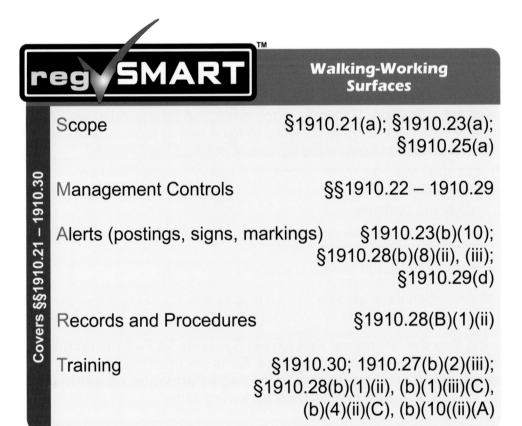

Covers §§1910.21 – 1910.30

Walking-Working Surfaces

Scope	§1910.21(a); §1910.23(a); §1910.25(a)
Management Controls	§§1910.22 – 1910.29
Alerts (postings, signs, markings)	§1910.23(b)(10); §1910.28(b)(8)(ii), (iii); §1910.29(d)
Records and Procedures	§1910.28(B)(1)(ii)
Training	§1910.30; 1910.27(b)(2)(iii); §1910.28(b)(1)(ii), (b)(1)(iii)(C), (b)(4)(ii)(C), (b)(10((ii)(A)

⟩ regSMART™ is especially helpful to the user because OSHA does not follow a pattern in its paragraph system. For instance, training requirements may be in paragraph (f) in one section and paragraph (g)(2) in another. Therefore, regSMART™ becomes a quick reference, particularly when looking for Alerts, Records, and Training requirements listed in the regulations.

General Requirements for Housekeeping

All places of employment, passageways, storerooms, service rooms, and walking-working surfaces must be kept in a clean, orderly, and sanitary condition.

Workroom floors must be kept clean and, to the extent feasible, dry. Drainage must be maintained if wet processes are used, and dry standing places, such as false floors, platforms, and mats, must be provided.

Walking-working surfaces must be free of hazards such as:

> sharp or protruding objects
> loose boards
> corrosion

> leaks and spills
> snow and ice

§1910.22(a)

Fall Protection

Each employee exposed to fall and falling object hazards must be provided fall protection. Generally, each employee on a walking-working surface where there is the potential to fall 4 feet or more to a lower level must be protected from falling by one or more of the following:

> guardrail systems (with toeboards if falling objects could be hazardous)
> safety net systems
> personal fall protection systems (e.g., personal fall arrest, travel restraint, or positioning system)
> covers (allowed in certain situations)

Fall protection must also be used if employees could fall 4 feet or more through openings or into or onto dangerous equipment from any height.

Note: See the "Personal Fall Arrest Systems as Fall Protection" handout in the Student Workbook for more information on personal fall arrest systems, including information on estimating fall distance, tie-off concerns, and swing falls.

§1910.28(a), (b)

Falling Object Protection

If falling objects are a hazard, head protection must be worn and one of the following must be used:

> toeboards, screens, or guardrail systems
> canopies
> barricades

§1910.28(c)

Toeboards used for falling object protection must:

> be erected along the exposed edge of the overhead walking-working surface for a length sufficient to protect employees below;

> be at least 3.5 inches tall (***Exception***: 2.5 inches when used around vehicle repair, service, or assembly pits);

> not have more than a 0.25-inch clearance or opening above the walking-working surface;

> be solid or not have any opening exceeding 1 inch at its greatest dimension;

> be capable of withstanding a force of at least 50 pounds;

> have paneling or screening installed above the toeboard to the mid-rail if tools equipment or materials are piled higher than the top of the toeboard (or to the top rail if items are piled higher than the midrail); and

> be used, if applicable, with guardrail systems having openings small enough to prevent objects from falling through.

Canopies used for falling object protection must be strong enough to prevent collapse and to prevent penetration by falling objects.

Requirements for Guardrails

Guardrails used for fall protection must:

> have top rails that are 42 inches (+/- 3 inches) above the surface;

> have midrails, screens, mesh, intermediate vertical members, solid panels, or equivalent intermediate members if there is no wall or parapet;

> be capable of withstanding a force of at least 200 pounds applied in any downward or outward direction within 2 inches of the top edge at any point along the rail;

> not be made of steel banding or plastic banding;

> be smooth-surfaced; and

> generally be installed on all unprotected sides or edges, except at the access (which generally must be offset or gated), with the fall hazard otherwise guarded if the guardrail (or section) is removed temporarily.

§1910.29(k)

§1910.29(b)

Stairways

Stairways must meet the following requirements (not a complete list):
- If there is an unprotected side or edge of a landing that is 4 feet or more above a lower level, there must be a guardrail or stair rail system.
- Each flight of stairs having at least 3 treads and at least 4 risers must be equipped with stair rails and handrails; requirements vary depending on the width of the stair and whether the stairway is enclosed, open on one side, or open on two sides.
- There must be at least 6 feet, 8 inches of vertical clearance between any stair tread and any overhead obstruction.

Stairways

Stairways must meet the following requirements (not a complete list): (continued)
- Stairs must be uniform in riser height and tread depth between landings.
- The swing of any door or gate onto a stairway platform must not reduce the platform's depth to less than 20 inches (if installed before 1/17/2017) or 22 inches (if installed on or after 1/17/2017).
  - Each stair must be able to support at least 5 times the anticipated load, but never less than 1,000 pounds.

§§1910.28(b)(11); 1910.25

Ladders in General

Ladders must meet these requirements (not a complete list):
- Rungs, steps, and cleats must be spaced 10 – 14 inches apart and must be parallel, level, and uniformly spaced when the ladder is positioned for use. There must be a minimum clear width of 11.5 inches for portable ladders and 16 inches for fixed.
- Wooden ladders may not be coated with any material that may obscure structural defects. Metal ladders must be protected against corrosion. All ladder surfaces must be free of puncture and laceration hazards.
- Rungs and steps on portable metal ladders must be treated to minimize slipping.

Ladders in General

Ladders must meet these requirements (not a complete list): (continued)
- Portable single-rail ladders are prohibited.
- Stepladders must have metal spreader or locking devices to keep them open when in use.
- Do **not** use fixed ladders having a pitch greater than 90° from the horizontal.

Ladder Safety and Use

Follow these rules:
- **Inspect before initial use** in each work shift and more frequently as necessary. Immediately tag any ladder with a structural or other defect with, "**Dangerous: Do Not Use,**" or similar language and **remove it from service** until repaired or replaced.

§1910.23

Stairways

Stairways must meet the following requirements (not a complete list):

> If there is an unprotected side or edge of a landing that is 4 feet or more above a lower level, there must be a guardrail or stair rail system.

> Each flight of stairs having at least 3 treads and at least 4 risers must be equipped with stair rails and handrails; requirements vary depending on the width of the stair and whether the stairway is enclosed, open on one side, or open on two sides.

> There must be at least 6 feet, 8 inches of vertical clearance between any stair tread and any overhead obstruction.

> Stairs must be uniform in riser height and tread depth between landings.

> The swing of any door or gate onto a stairway platform must not reduce the platform's depth to less than 20 inches (if installed before 1/17/2017) or 22 inches (if installed on or after 1/17/2017). Each stair must be able to support at least 5 times the anticipated load, but never less than 1,000 pounds.

Ladders in General

Ladders must meet these requirements (not a complete list):

> Rungs, steps, and cleats must be spaced 10 – 14 inches apart and must be parallel, level, and uniformly spaced when the ladder is positioned for use. There must be a minimum clear width of 11.5 inches for portable ladders and 16 inches for fixed.

> Wooden ladders may not be coated with any material that may obscure structural defects. Metal ladders must be protected against corrosion. All ladder surfaces must be free of puncture and laceration hazards.

> Rungs and steps on portable metal ladders must be treated to minimize slipping.

> Portable single-rail ladders are prohibited.

> Stepladders must have metal spreader or locking devices to keep them open when in use.

> Do **not** use fixed ladders having a pitch greater than 90° from the horizontal.

Ladder Safety and Use

Follow these rules:

> Inspect before initial use in each work shift and more frequently as necessary. Immediately tag any ladder with a structural or other defect with, "Dangerous: Do Not Use," or similar language and remove it from service until repaired or replaced.

> Use ladders only on stable, level surfaces unless secured or stabilized to prevent accidental displacement.

> Do **not** move, shift, or extend a ladder while an employee is on it.

> If ladders are used in locations such as passageways, doorways, or driveways where they can be displaced by other activities or traffic, either secure them to prevent displacement, or use a temporary barricade, such as a row of traffic cones or caution tape, to keep activities and traffic away.

> Do **not** use the top cap or top step of a stepladder as a step.

> Secure and stabilize portable ladders used on slippery surfaces.

> Place the top of a non-self-supporting ladder so that both side rails are supported unless the ladder is equipped with a single support attachment.

> Ensure that the side rails of portable ladders used to gain access to upper landing surfaces extend at least 3 feet above the upper landing surface.

> Unless specifically designed to do so, do not tie or fasten together ladders or ladder sections to add length.

> Do **not** place ladders on boxes, barrels, or other unstable bases to obtain additional height.

> Do **not** load a ladder beyond the maximum intended load, which includes the total load (weight and force) of the employee and all tools, equipment, and materials being carried.

> Ladders may be used only for the purpose for which they were designed.

> Face the ladder when climbing up or down it.

> Use at least one hand to grasp the ladder when climbing up or down it.

> Do **not** carry any object or load that could cause you to lose balance and fall while climbing up or down the ladder.

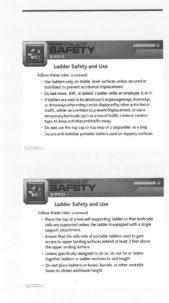

Fall Protection for Ladders

Fall protection is **not** required when using portable ladders. However, for fixed ladders that extend more than 24 feet above a lower level, fall protection is required, as follows:

> If installed before 11/19/2018, there must be a personal fall arrest system, ladder safety system (see below), cage, or well.

> If installed on or after 11/19/2018, there must be a personal fall arrest system or ladder safety system.

> When a fixed ladder, cage, well, or portion thereof is replaced, a personal fall arrest system or ladder safety system must be installed in at least that section.

> By 11/18/2036, all fixed ladders must have a personal fall arrest or ladder safety system.

§1910.21(b);
§1910.28(a)(2)(i), (b)(9)

§§1910.21(b); 1910.23(e)

A **ladder safety system** is a system designed to eliminate or reduce the possibility of falling from a ladder. The system usually consists of a carrier, safety sleeve, lanyard, connectors and body harness. **Note**: Cages and wells are not ladder safety systems.

When so equipped, the personal fall arrest system or ladder safety system must provide protection throughout the entire vertical distance of the ladder, including all sections. There must be rest platforms at least every 150 feet.

Any ladder section having a cage or well must be offset from adjacent sections and have landing platforms at least every 50 feet.

Mobile Ladder Stands

A **mobile ladder stand** is a mobile, fixed-height, self-supporting ladder usually consisting of wheels or casters on a rigid base and steps leading to a top step. It is designed for use by one employee at a time.

If you are using a mobile ladder stand, ensure:

» You use additional support (outriggers, counterweights, etc.) if the maximum work-surface height exceeds four times the shortest base dimension;

» It is not moved when anyone is on it; and

» It meets the additional requirements of §1910.23(e).

Dockboards

Dockboards must:

> be capable of supporting the maximum intended load;

> be designed, constructed, and maintained to prevent transfer vehicles from running off the dockboard edge (***Exception***: where there is no hazard of transfer vehicles running off the dockboard edge);

> secured by anchoring or using equipment that prevents the dockboard from moving out of a safe position, if portable;

> use measures such as wheel chocks or sand shoes to prevent the transport vehicle on which a dockboard is placed from moving while employees are on it;

> be equipped with handholds or other means to permit safe handling, if portable; and

> be used with fall protection (guardrail system or handrails) when there is a possibility of a fall 4 feet or more to a lower level.

§§1910.26; 1910.28(b)(4)

Scaffolds

All scaffolds used in general industry must meet OSHA requirements for the construction industry. Some of the more significant of these follow:

> Each scaffold and component must be able to support its own weight and at least four times its maximum intended load.

> Scaffolds must be designed by a qualified person and built and loaded to design.

> Each employee on a scaffold more than 10 feet above a lower level must have fall protection. Depending on the type of scaffold, fall protection must be provided by guardrails, a personal fall arrest system, or both. Personal fall arrest systems used on scaffolds must be attached by lanyard to a vertical lifeline, horizontal lifeline, or scaffold structural member.

> Each employee on a scaffold is required to wear a hardhat.

> Have a competent person inspect scaffolds and components for visible defects before each work shift and after any event that could affect scaffold integrity. Immediately remove, repair, or brace scaffolds and components if damaged or sub-standard.

> Maintain the following required distances for scaffolds near powerlines:

» 0 feet plus 0.4 inches for each 1kV over 50kV for uninsulated lines and insulated lines of 300 volts or more

» 3 feet for insulated lines less than 300 volts

> Erect, move, dismantle, or alter scaffolds only under supervision of a competent person and using experienced and trained employees selected by the competent person.

> Use tag lines to control swinging loads being hoisted onto or near scaffolds.

> Protect suspension ropes from heat-producing processes and corrosives or acids.

> Do **not** allow loads on scaffolds and components to exceed their maximum rated capacities.

> Do **not** use shore or lean-to scaffolds.

> Do **not** perform scaffold work during storms or in high winds unless a competent person determines that it is safe and employees use a personal fall arrest system or wind screens.

§1910.27(a);
§1926.451(a), (f), (g)

> Do **not** work on scaffolds coated with ice, snow, or slippery materials.
> Do **not** allow horizontal movement of scaffolds with employees on them unless designed specially by a registered engineer or moved properly with mobile scaffolds.

Note: **See the "Scaffold Access and Use," "Supported Scaffolds in General," "Suspension Scaffolds in General," "Fall Protection for Scaffolds," and "Scaffold Erection and Disassembly" handouts in the Student Workbook for more in-depth information on scaffolds.**

Rope Descent Systems

A **rope descent system** is a suspension system that allows an employee to descent in a controlled manner and, as needed, stop at any point during the descent. It usually consists of a roof anchorage, support rope, a descent device, carabiner(s) or shackle(s), and a chair/seatboard.

Rope descent systems:

> generally may **not** be used for heights greater than 300 feet;
> must be used in accordance with the manufacturer's instructions, warnings, and design limitations or under the direction of a qualified person;
> may be used only by properly trained employees;
> must be inspected at the start of each work shift on which it is used, with damaged or defective equipment immediately removed from service and replaced;
> must be properly rigged, particularly with tiebacks when counterweights, cornice hooks, or similar non-permanent anchorages are used;
> must be used with separate, independent personal fall arrest systems;
> must have all components capable of sustaining a minimum rated load of 5,000 pounds (live load of 300 pounds for seatboards);
> must be used with procedures that ensure prompt rescue in the event of a fall;
> must have ropes that are padded or protected from contact with edges of buildings, anchorages, obstructions, or other surfaces to prevent cuts or weakening;
> must have stabilization at the specific work location when descents are greater than 130 feet;
> must **not** be used during hazardous weather conditions;
> must be protected from exposure to open flames, hot work, corrosive chemicals, and other destructive conditions; and
> must be used with equipment (e.g., tools, squeegees, buckets) secured to prevent it from falling.

Module Four

Exit Routes, Emergency Action Plans, and Fire Prevention Plans

Covers 1910.34 – 1910.39

Exit Routes, Emergency Action Plans, and Fire Prevention Plans	
Scope	§1910.34(a), (b); §1910.35; §1910.38(a); §1910.39(a)
Management Controls	§§1910.35-1910.38
Alerts (postings, signs, markings)	§1910.37(b), (e); §1910.38(d); Appendix to Subpart E(1)
Records and Procedures	§1910.38(b), (c); §1910.39(a), (b)
Training	§1910.38(e), (f); §1910.39(d)

regSMART

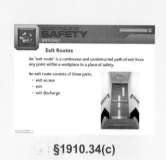

§1910.34(c)

§1910.35

§1910.36(a), (b)

§1910.36(c), (d)

Exit Routes

An "exit route" is a continuous and unobstructed path of exit from any point within a workplace to a place of safety.

An exit route consists of three parts:

> exit access

> exit

> exit discharge

An employer that demonstrates compliance with either of the following will be deemed to be in compliance with the requirements of §§1910.34, .35, and .36:

> NFPA 101, Life Safety Code (2009 edition)

> the exit route provisions of the International Fire Code (2009 edition)

Exit Route Requirements

Exit routes must:

> be permanent;

> be separated from other parts of the workplace by fire-resistant materials; and

> have limited openings.

At least two exit routes, as far away from each other as possible, must be available in a workplace to permit prompt evacuation of employees. One exit may be allowed, or more than two exits may be required, depending on:

> the number of employees;

> the size of the building;

> the building's occupancy; and/or

> the arrangement of the workplace.

Each exit discharge must lead directly outside or to a street, walkway, refuge area, public way, or open space with access to the outside. In addition:

> Exit doors must remain unlocked.

>> Employees must be able to open an exit route door from the inside at all times without keys, tools, or special knowledge. Devices that lock only from the outside, such as panic bars, are allowed.

> Exit doors must have side hinges.

> The capacity of the exit route must be adequate.

> The exit route must meet minimum height and width requirements.

>> Ceilings along the route must be at least 7.5 feet high. Any projection from the ceiling must not reach a point less than 6.75 feet from the floor.

>> Exit access must be at least 28 inches wide at all points.

§1910.36(e)-(g)

Keep in mind these additional requirements for exit routes:

> Exit routes must be kept free of explosive or highly flammable furnishings and decorations.

> Exit routes must be arranged to avoid high hazard areas.

> Exit routes must be free and unobstructed.

> Safeguards designed to protect employees during an emergency (e.g., sprinkler and alarm systems, fire doors, exit lighting, etc.) must be in proper working order at all times.

§1910.37(a)(1)-(4)

> Each exit route must be adequately lit.

> Exits must be marked.

> Each exit route door must be free from decorations or signs that obscure visibility.

> If the direction of travel to the exit is not immediately apparent, signs must be posted indicating the direction of travel.

§1910.37(b)(1)-(4)

> Each doorway or passageway that could be mistaken for an exit must be marked "Not an Exit" or with a similar warning.

> Exit signs must have letters at least 6 inches high with the principal strokes of the letters at least ¾ of an inch wide. Signs must also be illuminated.

> Exit routes must be maintained during construction, repairs, or alterations.

> Outdoor exit routes must be covered unless the employer can demonstrate timely snow and ice removal.

§1910.37(b)(5)-(7), (d)

§1910.37(e); §1910.165

§1910.38

Subpart E, Appendix

Employers must install and maintain an operable employee alarm system to warn employees of fire or other emergencies. This system must:

> have a distinct signal;

> allow for enough reaction time for safe escape;

> be explained to employees;

> have emergency telephone numbers posted near, if the system uses telephones; and

> be tested for reliability and adequacy at least every 2 months, if the system is not supervised.

Safety STOP™

OSHA Letter of Interpretation — Clarke 11/21/03

If an electronic key card fails, does this constitute obstructed access to an exit route? Pursuant to 29 CFR 1910.35, employers who wish to comply with the NFPA 101-2000, the Life Safety Code "Access-Controlled Egress Doors" standard (which addresses electronic swipe cards) will also be in compliance with corresponding requirements of OSHA's Exit Route Standard.

Emergency Action Plan

Requirements:

An employer must have an emergency action plan when an OSHA standard requires one.

An emergency action plan must be in writing, kept in the workplace, and available for employees to review.

Emergency action plans should address emergencies the employer may reasonably expect, such as:

> fire

> smoke

> toxic vapors

> explosion

> bomb threat

> terrorism

> flash floods

> nuclear radiation

> earthquake

> any other emergency

The following elements, at a minimum, shall be included in the plan:

> procedures for reporting a fire or other emergency

> procedures for emergency evacuation, including type of evacuation and exit route

> procedures to be followed by employees who remain to operate critical plant operations before they evacuate

> procedures to account for all employees after evacuation

> procedures to be followed by employees performing rescue or medical duties

> the name or job title of every employee who may be contacted by employees who may need more information about the plan or an explanation of their duties under the plan

Alarm System:

An employer must have and maintain an employee alarm system, as discussed previously.

Training:

An employer must designate and train employees to assist in a safe and orderly evacuation of other employees.

Generally, one warden for every 20 employees in the workplace should be able to provide adequate guidance and instruction in the event of a fire, or other, emergency. (See Subpart E Appendix.)

Review of Emergency Action Plan:

The employer must review the plan with each employee it covers:

> when the plan is developed or the employee is assigned initially to a job;

> when the employee's responsibilities under the plan change; and

> when the plan is changed.

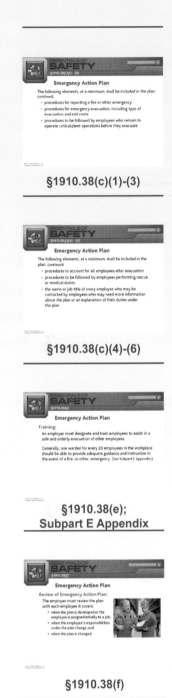

§1910.38(c)(1)-(3)

§1910.38(c)(4)-(6)

§1910.38(e);
Subpart E Appendix

§1910.38(f)

§1910.39(a), (b)

§1910.39(c)(1)

§1910.39(c)(2)-(5)

§1910.39(d)

Fire Prevention Plan

Requirements:

An employer must have a fire prevention plan when an OSHA standard requires one.

A fire prevention plan must be in writing, kept in the workplace, and available for employees to review.

Fire prevention plans must include:

> list of all major fire hazards

> proper handling and storage procedures

> potential ignition sources and their controls

> type of fire protection equipment necessary to control each major hazard

> procedures to control accumulation of hazardous waste material

> procedures for regular maintenance of safeguards on heat-producing equipment

> name and title of employees maintaining equipment

> name and title of employees in control of fuel source hazards

Employee Information:

An employer must:

> inform employees of the fire hazards to which they are exposed upon initial assignment to a job; and

> review with each employee the parts of the fire prevention plan necessary for self-protection.

Module Five
Fire Protection

regSMART™

Covers 1910.157	Fire Protection	
Scope	§1910.157(a), (b)
Management Controls	§1910.157
Alerts (postings, signs, markings)	§1910.157(c)(1)
Records and Procedures	§1910.157(e)(3), (f)(16)
Training	§1910.157(g)

regSMART

§1910.155(c)

§1910.157(c)(1)

Fires and Fire Protection

According to the Bureau of Labor Statistics, workplace fires and explosions kill 200 workers and injure more than 5,000 workers each year.

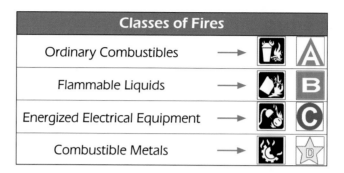

Classes of Fires		
Ordinary Combustibles	→	A
Flammable Liquids	→	B
Energized Electrical Equipment	→	C
Combustible Metals	→	D

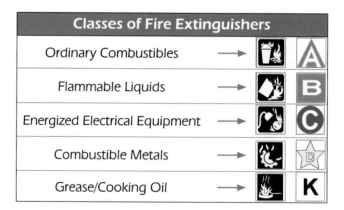

Classes of Fire Extinguishers		
Ordinary Combustibles	→	A
Flammable Liquids	→	B
Energized Electrical Equipment	→	C
Combustible Metals	→	D
Grease/Cooking Oil	→	K

Portable Fire Extinguishers

General Requirement:

Employers shall provide portable fire extinguishers and shall mount, locate, and identify them so they are readily accessible to employees without subjecting them to possible injury.

Exemptions:

The requirement to provide fire extinguishers and the requirements discussed in this module do not apply if the employer has:

> a written fire safety policy requiring the immediate and total evacuation of employees upon the sounding of the fire alarm;

> an emergency action plan;

> a fire prevention plan; and

> not made fire extinguishers available in the workplace.

If the employer has an emergency action plan that designates certain employees as the only employees authorized to use the available portable fire extinguishers and that requires all other employees in the fire area to immediately evacuate when the alarm sounds, then the employer is exempt from the selection and distribution requirements discussed in this module.

If the employer has provided fire extinguishers, but they are not intended for employee use, and the employer has an emergency action plan and fire prevention plan, then only the inspection, maintenance, and testing requirements and the hydrostatic testing requirements discussed in this module will apply.

Selection and Distribution:

Extinguishers must be selected and distributed based on:

> the classes of anticipated workplace fires; and

> the size and degree of the hazard.

Maximum allowed travel distance to portable fire extinguishers is based on the class of anticipated fires, as follows:

> **Class A (Ordinary Combustibles):** Distribute portable extinguishers for use on Class A fires so employee travel distance is no further than 75 feet.

> **Class B (Flammable Liquids):** Distribute portable extinguishers for use on Class B fires so that travel distance between the hazard and the extinguisher is 50 feet or less.

> **Class C (Energized Electrical Equipment):** Distribute portable extinguishers for Class C hazards based on the appropriate patterns for Class A or B hazards.

> **Class D (Combustible Metals):** Distribute portable extinguishers for Class D hazards within 75 feet of the hazard.

§1910.157(b)(1), (2)

§1910.157(d)(1)

§1910.157(d)(2), (4)

§1910.157(d)(5), (6)

§1910.157(e)(2), (3)

§1910.157(e)(4), (5)

§1910.157(g)(1)-(3)

NFPA

Inspections, Maintenance, and Testing:

When performing fire extinguisher inspections, follow these requirements:

> Visually inspect portable fire extinguishers monthly.

> Assure all portable fire extinguishers have an annual maintenance check.

> Assure stored pressure dry chemical extinguishers that require a 12-year hydrostatic test are emptied and subjected to applicable maintenance procedures every 6 years.

> Assure that alternate equivalent protection is provided when portable fire extinguishers are removed from service for maintenance and recharging.

> Hydrostatically test portable extinguishers as required in §1910.157(f).

Training:

Where the employer has provided portable fire extinguishers for employee use in the workplace, the employer shall provide:

> an educational program to familiarize employees with the general principles of fire extinguisher use and the hazards involved with incipient stage firefighting;

> firefighting education upon initial employment and at least annually thereafter; and

> firefighting education to employees designated to use firefighting equipment as part of an emergency action plan with training in the use of the appropriate equipment.

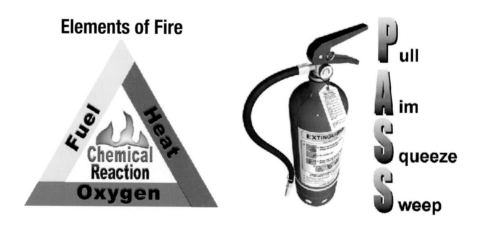

Elements of Fire

Module Six
Electrical Cords

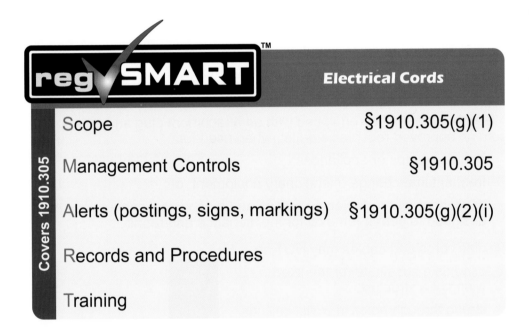

Electrical Cords

Covers 1910.305

Scope	§1910.305(g)(1)
Management Controls	§1910.305
Alerts (postings, signs, markings)	§1910.305(g)(2)(i)
Records and Procedures	
Training	

§1910.305(g)(1)(i)

§1910.305(g)(1)(ii)

§1910.305(g)(1)(iii)

§1910.305(g)(1)(iv)

§1910.305(g)(2)

Use of Flexible Cords and Cables

Flexible cords and cables shall be approved and suitable for conditions of use and location.

Flexible cords and cables shall be used only for the following:

› pendants

› wiring of fixtures

› connections of portable lamps or appliances

› elevator cables

› wiring of cranes and hoists

› connection of stationary equipment to facilitate their frequent interchange

› prevention of noise or vibration

› appliances, where designed to permit removal

› data processing cables

A flexible cord shall be equipped with an attachment plug and energized from an approved receptacle outlet, when used for:

› portable lamps or appliances;

› frequent interchange of stationary equipment; or

› appliances where fastening means and mechanical connections are designed to permit removal for maintenance and repair.

Flexible cords and cables may NOT be:

› used as a substitute for the fixed wiring of a structure;

› strung through holes in walls, ceilings, or floors;

› placed through doorways, windows, etc.;

› attached to building surfaces; nor

› concealed behind building walls, ceilings, or floors.

Cords may NOT be repaired with electrical tape. If repaired, they must be returned to their original mechanical integrity and insulating properties.

A conductor of a flexible cord or cable used as a grounded conductor or an equipment grounding conductor shall be distinguishable from other conductors.

Use of Extension Cords

There is usually no question about use of the short length of cord furnished as part of an approved appliance or tool.

There is usually no question about an extension cord used temporarily to permit use of the appliance or tool in its intended manner at some distance from a fixed outlet.

But there are questions when the usage is not obviously temporary or when the cord is extended to some distant outlet in order to avoid providing a fixed outlet where needed.

Flexible cords used in violation of this standard are likely to be damaged by activities in the area such as:

> door or window edges

> staples or fastenings

> abrasion from adjacent materials

> aging

If the conductors become partially exposed over a period of time, there will be a danger of shocks, burns, or fire. Use temporary electrical power and lighting installations only for:

> remodeling, maintenance, repair, or demolition of buildings, structures, or equipment, and similar activities;

> experimental or development work; and

> a period not to exceed 90 days for Christmas decorative lighting, carnivals, and similar purposes.

Splices:

Flexible cords shall be used only in continuous lengths without splice or tap. Hard service flexible cords No. 14 and larger may be repaired if spliced so the splice retains:

> insulation;

> outer sheath properties; and

> usage characteristics of the cord being spliced.

Termination:

Flexible cords shall be connected to devices and fittings so that strain relief is provided, which will prevent pull from being directly transmitted to joints or terminal screws.

Power Strips

OSHA regulations require that listed or labeled equipment be installed and used in accordance with any instructions included in the listing or labeling.

OSHA Electrical Training

§1910.305(a)(2)(i)

§1910.305(g)(2)(ii)

§1910.305(g)(2)(iii)

§1910.303(b)(2);
UL Directory

LOI - 11/18/02: Abnett

Manufacturers and nationally recognized testing laboratories determine the proper uses for power strips. For example, the Underwriters Laboratories (UL) Directory contains instructions that require UL-listed power strips:

> to be directly connected to a permanently installed branch circuit receptacle outlet;

> are not to be series-connected to other power strips or to extension cords; and

> are not intended to be used at construction sites and similar locations.

Notes:

> A "nationally recognized testing laboratory" is an organization recognized by OSHA that tests equipment or materials for safety and then lists, labels, or accepts it.

> Equipment is "listed" if it is mentioned in a list published by a nationally recognized testing laboratory.

> Equipment is "labeled" if it has a label, symbol, or other identifying mark of a nationally recognized testing laboratory.

> Equipment is "accepted" if it has been inspected and found by a nationally recognized testing laboratory to conform to specified plans or procedures of applicable codes.

OSHA regulations also require that outlet devices have an ampere rating not less than the load to be served. Power strips are designed for use with a number of low-powered loads, such as computers, peripherals, or audio/video components. Power strips are NOT designed for high-power loads such as space heaters, refrigerators, microwaves, etc., which can easily exceed the recommended ampere ratings on many power strips.

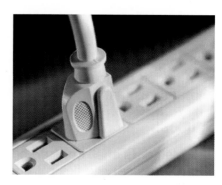

Safety STOP ™

OSHA Letter of Interpretation — 11/18/02: Abnett

"Surge/Spike Protectors" or "Portable Outlets"
Typically these consist of several components, such as multiple electrical receptacles, on/off power switch, circuit breaker, and a grounded flexible power cord. Power strips are typically designed for electronic equipment that has a low-powered load.

Module Seven

Recordkeeping and Reporting, Part 1

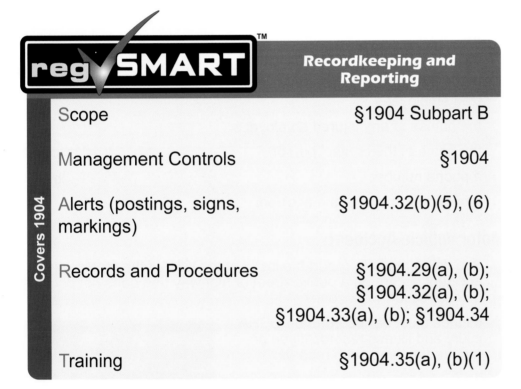

regSMART™	**Recordkeeping and Reporting**
Scope	§1904 Subpart B
Management Controls	§1904
Alerts (postings, signs, markings)	§1904.32(b)(5), (6)
Records and Procedures	§1904.29(a), (b); §1904.32(a), (b); §1904.33(a), (b); §1904.34
Training	§1904.35(a), (b)(1)

Covers 1904

§1904.39(a)

§1904.39(b)(2)

§1904.39(b)(3)

§1904.39(b)(4)

Reporting

Employers are required to report the following to OSHA:

> any employee fatalities (within 8 hours);

> any-work related in-patient hospitalization (within 24 hours); or

> all work-related amputations or losses of an eye (within 24 hours).

Report these by phone (1-800-321-OSHA or to the nearest OSHA Area Office during normal business hours) or through the OSHA website (https://www.osha.gov/pls/ser/serform.html).

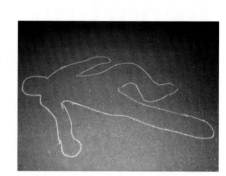

The report must include:

> the name of the establishment

> the time and location of the incident

> the number of fatalities or hospitalized employees

> the names of any injured employees

> the name of the contact person

> a phone number

> a brief description of the accident

Motor Vehicle Accident:

> You do not have to report the incident to OSHA if the motor vehicle accident occurs on a public street or highway and does not occur in a construction work zone.

> Injuries must be recorded on OSHA injury and illness records if you are required to keep such records.

Commercial or Public Transportation:

> You do not have to call OSHA to report a fatality or inpatient hospitalization, amputation, or loss of an eye.

> Injuries must be recorded on OSHA injury and illness records if you are required to keep such records.

Fatalities Caused by Heart Attacks at Work:

> Report to your local OSHA area office director and he or she will decide whether to investigate the incident, depending on the circumstances of the heart attack.

§1904.39(b)(5)

Fatality or Hospitalization That Occurs Long After the Incident:

> If the fatality or multiple hospitalization incident occurs within 30 days of the incident, you must report it.

> If the fatality or multiple hospitalization incident occurs 30 or more days after the incident, you are not required to report it.

§1904.39(b)(6)

Recordkeeping

OSHA forms 301, 300, and 300-A, or equivalent forms, must be used to record injuries and illnesses. Every item on a 300 Log will have a 301 Injury and Illness Incident Report.

Refer to the OSHA 301 Form, OSHA 300 Form, and the OSHA 300A Form in the Student Workbook.

§1904.29(a), (b)(2); §1904.41

Effective January 1, 2017, certain employers will be required to electronically submit the injury and illness data they are already required to record on their onsite OSHA injury and illness forms. Some of the data will also be posted to the OSHA website to encourage employers to improve workplace safety and provide information to workers, job seekers, customers, researchers, and the general public; however, OSHA will remove any personally identifiable information before the data is released to the public. The amount of data submitted will vary depending on the size of the copy and type of industry. OSHA plans to provide a secure website for the electronic submissions. The website will include web forms for direct data entry and instructions for other means of submission (e.g., file uploads).

§1904.1(a)(1)

§1904.2; Appendix A to Subpart B of §1904

Step 1: Are You Required to Maintain a 300 Log?

Companies with 10 or fewer employees at all times during the previous calendar year are not required to maintain a 300 Log. This is a company-wide employee count that includes workers who are full-time, hourly, salaried, part-time, temporary, or seasonal. Use peak employment numbers when counting employees.

Certain "low hazard" industries are partially exempt and are not required to maintain a 300 Log:

NAICS code	Industry Description	NAICS code	Industry Description	NAICS code	Industry Description
4412	Other Motor Veh. Dealers.	5211	Monetary Authorities.	6113	Colleges & Universities.
4431	Electronics & App Stores.	5221	Dep. Credit Intermediation.	6114	Bus.,Comp & Mgmt Trng.
4461	Hlth & Personal Care Stores.	5222	Nondep. Credit Intermed.	6115	Tech. & Trade Schools.
4471	Gasoline Stations.	5223	Act. Rel. to Credit Intermed.	6116	Other Schools & Instruction.
4481	Clothing Stores.	5231	Sec. & Comm Contracts.	6117	Educational Support Svcs.
4482	Shoe Stores.	5232	Sec & Comm. Exchanges.	6211	Offices of Physicians.
4483	Jewelry, & Luggage Stores.	5239	Other Fin. Invest. Activities.	6212	Offices of Dentists.
4511	Sporting & Hobby Stores.	5241	Insurance Carriers.	6213	Offices Health Practitioners.
4512	Book & Music Stores.	5242	Agencies, & Brokerages.	6214	Outpatient Care Centers.
4531	Florists.	5251	Ins. & Emp. Benefit Funds.	6215	Medical & Diagnostic Labs
4532	Office Supp. & Gift Stores.	5259	Other Invest. Pools & Fund.	6244	Child Day Care Services.
4812	Nonscheduled Air Trans.	5312	Offices of Real Estate.	7114	Agents for Athlts & Entertain.
4861	Pipeline Trans. of Crude Oil.	5331	Less. of Intangible Assets.	7115	Indep, Artists & Writers.
4862	Pipeline Trans. of Nat. Gas.	5411	Legal Services.	7213	Room & Boarding Houses.
4869	Other Pipeline Trans.	5412	Acc, Tax Prep., & Payroll.	7221	Full-Service Restaurants.
4879	Scenic & Sightseeing Trans.	5413	Architectural & Engineering.	7222	Limited-Svc Eating Places.
4885	Freight Trans. Arrangement.	5414	Spec. Design Services.	7224	Drinking Places (Alcohol).
5111	Newspaper & Book Pub.	5415	Comp. Systems Design.	8112	Elect & Prec. Eq. Repair.
5112	Software Publishers.	5416	Mgmt, Sci., & Tech Svcs.	8114	Household Goods Repair.
5121	Motion Pict. & Video Ind.	5417	Sci. Research and Dev.	8121	Personal Care Services.
5122	Sound Recording Industries.	5418	Advertising & Related.	8122	Death Care Services.
5151	Radio and TVBroadcasting.	5511	Mgmt of Companies.	8131	Religious Organizations.
5172	Wireless Carriers.	5611	Office Admin. Services.	8132	Grant & Giving Services.
5173	Telecomm. Resellers.	5614	Business Support Services.	8133	Social Advocacy Orgs.
5179	Other Telecommunications.	5615	Travel and Reservation.	8134	Civic & Social Orgs.
5181	Internet Service Providers.	5616	Investigation and Security.	8139	Bus, Prof., Labor & Pol Orgs.
5182	Data Proc, Host. & Related.	6111	Elem. & Sec.Schools.		
5191	Other Information Services.	6112	Junior Colleges.		

Note: These establishments are not exempt from OSHA, just from recordkeeping on the 300 Log for occupational injuries and illnesses.

Defining an Establishment:

> An establishment is a single physical location where business is conducted or where services or industrial operations are performed.

>> **Note:** Each establishment must maintain a separate 300 Log.

> Can one business location include two or more establishments?

>> **YES.** Two or more separate businesses that share a single location can be separate establishments when special requirements are met.

> Can an establishment include more than one physical location?

>> **YES.** Two or more physical locations can be combined into a single establishment when special requirements are met.

§1904.46

Step 2: Is This Person Recordable?

You must record injuries and illnesses of all employees on your payroll, whether they are:

> labor

> executive

> hourly

> salary

> part-time

> seasonal

> migrant workers

§1904.31(a)

You must record injuries and illnesses that happen to workers not on your payroll if you provide day-to-day supervision. Examples include workers from a temporary help service, employee leasing service, personnel supply service, or a contractor.

§1904.31(b)(2)-(4)

§1904.5(a)

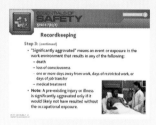

§1904.5(b)(4)

§1904.5(b)(2)

Step 3: Is This Case Work-Related?

It is work-related if the work environment caused or contributed to the resulting condition or significantly aggravated a pre-existing injury or illness. **Unless an exception (listed below) applies, all injuries and illnesses resulting from events or exposures occurring in the work environment are presumed to be work-related.**

> "Work-related" includes:
>> physical locations,
>> equipment used in course of work, and
>> materials used in course of work.

> "Significantly aggravated" means an event or exposure in the work environment that results in any of the following:

>> death
>> loss of consciousness
>> one or more days away from work, days of restricted work, or days of job transfer
>> medical treatment

> **Note:** A pre-existing injury or illness is significantly aggravated only if it would likely not have resulted without the occupational exposure.

An Injury or Illness Is Not Recordable If:

> The person experiencing the symptoms is in the workplace as a member of the general public.

> The symptoms happen at work, but result from a non-work-related event.

> It results from voluntary participation in wellness or recreation programs.

> It results from consuming food or drink, unless it was food or drink contaminated by workplace toxins or food supplied by the employer.

> It results from performing personal tasks outside working hours.

> It results from personal grooming, self-medication of a non-work related event, or it is intentionally self-inflicted.

> It results from a motor vehicle accident involving a moving, personally-owned (i.e., not company-owned) vehicle on a company parking lot or company access road as the employee was commuting to or from work.

> The illness is the cold or flu.

> The illness is a mental illness.

Working at Home

Even though an injury or illness occurred at home, if the answer to all of the following questions is "yes," the case is work-related and recordable:

> Was the employee working at home or at a home office at the time he or she became injured or ill?

> Was the employee being paid or compensated for the work?

> Was the injury or illness directly related to performing the work, rather than to the general home environment?

Work-Related	Not Work-Related
dropping a box of work documents and hurting a foot	tripping on the family dog while running to answer a work phone call
puncturing a finger while using a sewing machine at home to do garment work for the employer	being electrocuted because of faulty home wiring

Step 4: Is This a New Case?

It is a new case if:

> you have not previously recorded an incident for that employee;

OR

> you have a recordable incident for that employee of the same part of the body, but he or she recovered and was released to resume full duties.

§1904.5(b)(2)

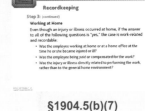

§1904.5(b)(7)

§1904.6(a)

Step 5: Is This Case Recordable?

Injuries:

> Injuries include cases such as, but not limited to:
>> cuts
>> fractures
>> sprains
>> amputations

Illnesses:

§1904.46

> Illnesses include both acute and chronic cases such as, but not limited to:
>> skin diseases
>> respiratory disorders
>> poisoning
>> hearing loss

Are paper cuts occupational injuries?

§1904.7(b)

> YES.

Do we need to record them?

§1904.7(b)(1)

> NO, not unless they require:
>> medical treatment beyond first aid,
>> transfer to another job, or
>> restriction of job.

A work-related injury or illness must be recorded if it results in one or more of the following:

> death
> days away from work
> restricted work or motion
> transfer to another job
> loss of consciousness
> significant diagnosis

> needlesticks and sharps injuries:
>> if contaminated by another person's blood or other fluids
> medical treatment beyond first aid
> medical removal under an OSHA standard

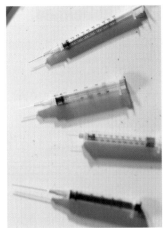

Medical Treatment Defined:

"Medical treatment" is the management and care of a patient to combat disease or disorder.

The following are considered to be medical treatment:

> prescription medication
> immunization shots, such as:
>> hepatitis B or rabies vaccines
> closing wounds with devices, such as:
>> sutures, staples, or surgical glue

> rigid immobilizing supports, such as:
>> devices with rigid stays
> removing foreign material from the eye with tweezers or other similar means
> physical therapy
> chiropractic treatment

The following is NOT medical treatment:

> visits to physicians or other health care providers solely for observation or counseling
> diagnostic procedures, such as:
>> x-rays, blood tests, or the administration of prescription medications used solely for diagnostic purposes
> first-aid treatments

§1904.7(b)(5); §1904.8(a); §1904.9(a)

§1904.7(b)(5)(i)

§1904.5(b)(5)(ii)

§1904.7(b)(5)(i)

First Aid Defined:

The following are considered first aid:

> non-prescription medications, such as:

>> over-the-counter in non-prescription strength aspirin

> tetanus shots

> cleaning, flushing, or soaking surface wounds

> wound coverings, such as:

>> bandages, gauze pads, butterfly strips, and Steri-strips™

> hot or cold therapy

> non-rigid supports, such as:

>> elastic bandages, wraps, and non-rigid back belts

> temporary supports for transportation, such as:

>> splints, slings, and neck collars

> drilling nail to relieve pressure

> draining fluid from blister

> eye patches

> removal of foreign bodies from eye with irrigation or cotton swab

> removal of splinters (other than from the eye) with tweezers

> finger guards

> massages

> drinking fluids to relieve heat stress

Note: This is a complete list of all treatments to be considered first aid.

Recording Needlesticks and Sharps Injuries

All work-related needlestick injuries and cuts from sharp objects that are contaminated with another person's blood or other potentially infectious material must be recorded.

> Enter the case on the 300 Log as an injury.

> Don't forget the Sharps Injury Log (see §1910.1030(h)(5)).

To protect the employee's privacy:

> Do NOT enter the employee's name (or job title if it reveals his or her identity) on the 300 Log.

> Enter the words "Privacy Case" instead.

Recording Hearing Loss

Job-related hearing losses must be recorded if they meet both of the following criteria:

> reflect a standard threshold shift (STS) (which is a change in hearing threshold, relative to the baseline audiogram for that employee) of an average of 10 decibels (dB) in one or both ears at 2,000, 3,000, and 4,000 hertz; and

> result in a total hearing level that is 25 dB or more from "audiometric zero" (which is the statistically average hearing of young adults without hearing problems).

The presence of an STS is determined by measuring the employee's hearing relative to his or her baseline audiogram.

> Employers may subtract for hearing loss caused by aging when determining if a 10-dB STS has occurred.

> Employers may not adjust for aging in determining whether the employee's hearing level is 25 dB or more from audiometric zero.

Employers do not have to record an STS if:

> they retest the employee's hearing within 30 days of the first test; and

> the retest does not confirm the STS.

To enter a recordable hearing loss case on the 300 Log, check the 300 Log column for hearing loss.

> The hearing loss must be work-related for it to be entered on the 300 Log.

> If a physician or other licensed health care professional determines the hearing loss is not work-related or has not been significantly aggravated by occupational noise exposure, the case does not have to be recorded on the OSHA 300 Log.

§1904.8(a)

§1904.10(a), (b)(1)

§1904.10(b)(1), (3)

§1904.10(b)(4)

§1904.10(b)(5), (6)

§1904.7(b)(6)

§1904.29(b)(6), (7)

§1904.7(b)(3), (6)

Recording Loss of Consciousness

If a work-related injury or illness leads to loss of consciousness, it is always recordable. This is true no matter how brief the period of unconsciousness.

Step 6: How Do I Complete the 300 Log?

Please refer to the Form 300 Log in your Student Workbook.

To fill out the 300 Log for a recordable injury or illness, do the following:

› Fill in the employee's name, unless the incident involves a privacy concern case involving one or more of the following:

» an intimate body part or the reproductive system

» sexual assault

» mental illness

» HIV infection, hepatitis, or tuberculosis

» needlestick or sharps injuries involving blood or other potentially infectious materials

» other illnesses for which the employee independently and voluntarily requests that his or her name not be entered on the Log

› **Note:** In addition, the employer must keep a separate privacy concern list containing the employees' names and case numbers for all privacy cases. This separate list is kept so that the employer may update the case or provide the information to the government if asked.

› Identify all of the following with respect to the incident:

» date of occurrence

» place of occurrence

» brief injury description

› Classify the seriousness of the case (from most to least):

» death

» days away from work

» job transfer or job restriction

» other recordable cases

› Identify the number of days away from work or on job transfer or restriction:

» Don't include the day on which the injury occurred or the illness began.

» Count calendar days, not scheduled work days. Weekend days, holidays, vacation days, or other days off are included in the total number of days recorded if the employee would not have been able to work on those days because of a work-related injury or illness.

» Count work from home as days away from work if an injured employee performs services for the company from home as a condition of his/her medical restriction (if that employee does not work from home as part of his or her normal work schedule).

» Consider an employee to be on restricted work if the employee is unable to perform one or more routine job functions, the employee is unable to work a full work day that he/she was otherwise scheduled to work, or a physician or other licensed health care professional recommends against working a full work day or performing one or more routine job functions.

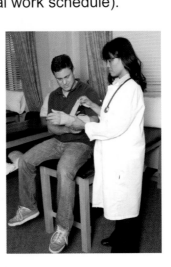

» Enter the total days for both days away and restricted work if a single case involves both.

» Apply a 180-day cap once the total of days off work or on restricted activity (either individually or in combination) reaches 180.

› Identify the case as an injury or illness and check the appropriate category for any illness.

Step 7: How Do I Update a Case?

If there are changes to the case during a 5-year period, you must update the original 300 Log entry to show these changes. Also enter on the original 300 Log any newly discovered recordable injuries or illnesses. (See §1904.33(b) for information on updating records.)

Step 8: How Do I Complete, Display, and Retain Forms?

The employer:

› has 7 calendar days to initiate entries on the log;

› has until the end of the next business day to provide copy of records to employee requests;

§1904.7(b)(3)

§1904.33

§1904.29(b)(3), .35(b)(2)(iii); §1904.32

§1904.32(b)(2)(i), (b)(3), (4)

§1904.32(b)(5), (6)

§1904.35(a)

§1904.36

> has no direct requirement to keep records onsite, but has 4 business hours to give records to a government representative; and

> must maintain all logs for 5 years beyond the current year.

OSHA 300 Log

> Summarize and total all columns at the end of the year.

>> Place "zeros" in empty columns.

> Do not post the 300 Log.

OSHA 300A Report

> The 300A Report must be examined and certified by a company executive (officer of corporation, owner of a sole proprietorship or partnership, highest-ranking company official working at the site, or his/her immediate supervisor).

> Post the 300A annual summary for the previous year.

>> Post each establishment's summary only within that establishment.

>> The 300A summary report must be posted from February 1 to April 30.

Employee Involvement

Your employees and their representatives must be involved in the recordkeeping system in several ways:

> You must inform each employee of how he or she is to report an injury or illness to you.

> You must provide limited access to your injury and illness records for your employees and their representatives.

Employees are protected under the Section 11(c) of the OSH Act:

> from retaliation for reporting injuries, illnesses, or fatalities;

> from retaliation for filing a safety and health complaint;

> for asking for access to Part 1904 records; and

> for exercising any other rights.

Module Eight

Access to Employee Exposure and Medical Records

Covers 1910.1020

reg✓SMART™	Access to Employee Exposure and Medical Records
Scope	§1910.1020(b)
Management Controls	§1910.1020
Alerts (postings, signs, markings)	§1910.1020(e)(3)(ii)
Records and Procedures	§1910.1020(d), (e)(3)(ii), (h)
Training	§1910.1020(g)(1)

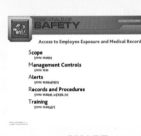

Access to Employee Exposure and Medical Records

Scope
§1910.1020(b)
Management Controls
§1910.1020
Alerts
§1910.1020(e)(3)(ii)
Records and Procedures
§1910.1020(d), (e)(3)(ii), (h)
Training
§1910.1020(g)(1)

regSMART

Medical and Exposure Records

Purpose

> To provide employees and their designated representatives a right of access to relevant exposure and medical records

Why maintain these records?

> To yield both direct and indirect improvements in the detection, treatment, and prevention of occupational disease

Who can maintain these records?

> Employer; or

> Can be carried out on behalf of employer by:

>> Physician, or

>> Health care professional in charge of employee medical records

Note: Nothing in this section is intended to affect existing legal and ethical obligations concerning the maintenance and confidentiality of employee medical information.

Don't forget about
HIPAA
Health Insurance Portability and Accountability Act

Scope

> Regulations regarding access to employee exposure and medical records apply to all general industry, construction, and maritime employers who make, maintain, contract, or have access to employee exposure or medical records, or analyses thereof, pertaining to employees exposed to toxic substances or harmful physical agents.

> The regulations apply to all employee exposure and medical records and analyses of employees:

Medical and Exposure Records

Purpose
- To provide employees and their designated representatives a right of access to relevant exposure and medical records

Medical and Exposure Records

Why maintain these records?
- To yield both direct and indirect improvements in the detection, treatment, and prevention of occupational disease

Medical and Exposure Records

Who can maintain these records?
- Employer; or
- Can be carried out on behalf of employer by:
  - Physician, or
  - Health care professional in charge of employee medical records. Nothing in this section is intended to affect existing legal and ethical obligations concerning the maintenance and confidentiality of employee medical information.

§1910.1020(a)

Medical and Exposure Records

Scope
- Regulations regarding access to employee exposure and medical records apply to all general industry, construction, and maritime employers who:
  - make;
  - maintain;
  - contract; or
  - have access to employee exposure or medical records or analyses thereof, pertaining to employees exposed to toxic substances or harmful physical agents.

§1910.1020(b)

Medical and Exposure Records

Scope (continued)
- The regulations apply to all employee exposure and medical records and analyses of employees:
  - whether or not the records are mandated by specific occupational safety and health standards, and
  - regardless of the manner in which the records are made or maintained.

§1910.1020(b)(2), (3)

» whether or not the records are mandated by specific occupational safety and health standards, and

» regardless of the manner in which the records are made or maintained.

Definitions

› Employee exposure record:

» Means a record containing any of the following kinds of information:

› environmental (workplace) monitoring

› biological monitoring results

› safety data sheets

§1910.1020(c)(5)

› Employee medical record:

» Means a record concerning the health status of an employee that is made or maintained by a physician, nurse, or other health care personnel or technician, including:

› medical and employment questionnaires

› results of medical examinations

› medical opinions, diagnoses, progress notes, and recommendations

› first aid records, which include medical histories

› descriptions of treatments and prescriptions

› employee medical complaints

§1910.1020(c)(6)

» "Employee medical record" does **not** include:

› physical specimens that are routinely discarded as a part of normal medical practice (e.g., blood or urine samples)

› records concerning health insurance claims, if maintained separately from the employer's medical program and its records, and if not accessible to the employer by employee name or other direct personal identifier (e.g., Social Security number, payroll number, etc.)

› records created solely in preparation for litigation that are privileged from discovery under the applicable rules of procedure or evidence

§1910.1020(c)(6)(ii)

§1910.1020(c)(6)(ii)

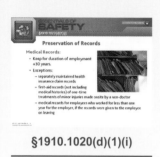

§1910.1020(d)(1)(i)

§1910.1020(d)(1)(ii)

> › records concerning voluntary employee assistance programs (alcohol, drug abuse, or personal counseling programs), if maintained separately from the employer's medical program and its records

Preservation of Records

Medical Records:

› Keep for duration of employment +30 years.

› Exceptions:

» separately maintained health insurance claim records

» first-aid records (not including medical histories) of one-time treatments of minor injuries made onsite by a non-doctor

» medical records for employees who worked for less than one year for the employer, if the records were given to the employee on leaving

Exposure Records:

› Keep for 30 years.

› Background data must be kept in some cases.

› Biological monitoring:

» Monitoring results that are non-detectable or below the permissible exposure limit of a substance are still considered employee exposure records that have to be preserved and maintained for 30 years.

» Employee exposure records that indicate an employee is exposed below the applicable action level or PEL are also part of the employee exposure record that must be preserved for 30 years.

Safety Data Sheets:

> Safety data sheets (SDSs) need not be retained for any specified period as long as a record is retained for at least 30 years that includes:

>> identity of the chemical

>> where it was used

>> when it was used

> Employers might simplify their responsibilities as they relate to the overlap between HazCom and access to records:

>> The list of hazardous chemicals could include information on where chemicals were used and when they were used. These lists would then have to be kept for at least 30 years.

§1910.1020(d)(1)(ii)[B]

§1910.1020(d)(1)(ii)[B], (d)(1)(iii)

Safety STOP™

OSHA Letter of Interpretation — 10/01/87: Robinson

An alternative to keeping both data sheets, however, is provided for in 29 CFR 1910.1020. Under paragraph (d)(1)(ii)[B] of this standard, employers may discard safety data sheets if a record identifying the substances and where and when they were used is retained for at least 30 years.

Analyses Using Medical or Exposure Records:

> These must be preserved and maintained for at least 30 years.

§1910.1020(e)(1)(i)

Access to Records

Whenever an employee or designated representative requests access to a record:

> Access must be provided within 15 working days.

> If the employer cannot reasonably provide access within 15 days, the affected employee must be notified of the reason for the delay and the earliest date when access will be given.

> Employees have the right to a copy of the requested record at no charge. Employers must either:

>> provide a copy at no cost, or

>> furnish photocopying facilities without charge.

§1910.1020(e)(1)(iii)

§1910.1020(e)(3)

§1910.1020(g)

§1910.1020(h)

OSHA Access:

Whenever OSHA requests access to a record:

› OSHA procedures generally require a written access order from an Assistant Secretary of Labor before the agency obtains employee medical information in a personally identifiable form.

» The employer must post a copy of the written access order (not identifying specific employees by direct personal identifier) and accompanying cover letter for at least 15 working days before access is granted.

› No order is required if an affected employee specifically consents in writing to allow OSHA access.

› No order is required for an OSHA staff physician to consult with the employer's physician on an occupational safety or health issue.

Employee Information

When an employee first enters into employment, and at least annually thereafter, he or she must be informed of the following:

› the existence, location, and availability of any records

› the person responsible for maintaining and providing access to records

› each employee's right to access his or her records

Copies of §1910.1020 must be made available to employees upon request.

Transfer of Records

When an employer ceases to do business and sells to another party, all medical and exposure records must be transferred to the new employer, who must receive and maintain them.

When an employer ceases to do business and there is no successor, the employer must notify affected current employees of their right of access to the records at least 3 months prior to the business closing date.

Module Nine
Bloodborne Pathogens

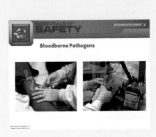

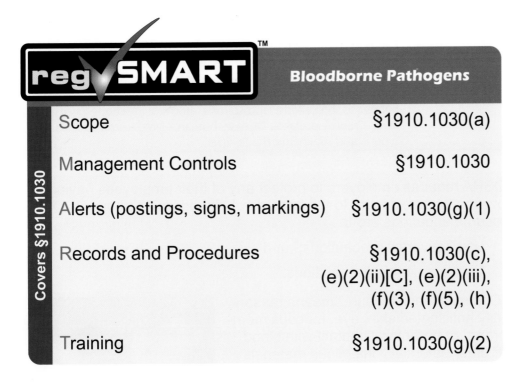

reg✔SMART™

Covers §1910.1030

Bloodborne Pathogens	
Scope	§1910.1030(a)
Management Controls	§1910.1030
Alerts (postings, signs, markings)	§1910.1030(g)(1)
Records and Procedures	§1910.1030(c), (e)(2)(ii)[C], (e)(2)(iii), (f)(3), (f)(5), (h)
Training	§1910.1030(g)(2)

Bloodborne Pathogens

Bloodborne pathogens are pathogenic microorganisms that are present in human blood and can infect and cause disease in humans. These pathogens include, but are not limited to, hepatitis B (HBV), hepatitis C (HCV), and human immunodeficiency virus (HIV).

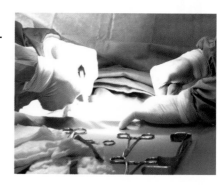

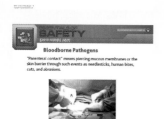

§1910.1030(b), (d)(1)

§1910.1030(d)(1)

OSHA Note

While HBV and HIV are specifically identified in the Bloodborne Pathogens Standard, the term includes any pathogenic microorganism that is present in human blood and can infect and cause disease in persons who are exposed to blood containing the pathogen. Other examples include hepatitis C, malaria, syphilis, babesiosis, brucellosis, leptospirosis, arboviral infections, relapsing fever, Creutzfeldt-Jakob Disease, human T-lymphotrophic virus type 1, and viral hemorrhagic fever.

OSHA requires employers to protect any of their employees having occupational exposure to the hazards of bloodborne pathogens. OSHA's recommendations are to:

> use "universal precautions;" and

> treat everything as infectious.

"Occupational exposure" means reasonably anticipated skin, eye, mucous membrane, or parenteral contact with blood or other potentially infectious materials that may result from the performance of an employee's duties.

"Parenteral contact" means piercing mucous membranes or the skin barrier through such events as needlesticks, human bites, cuts, and abrasions.

"Universal Precautions" require ALL blood and other potentially infectious materials to ALWAYS be treated as infectious. In other words, employees must use appropriate protective procedures and equipment EVERY TIME they may be exposed to bloodborne pathogens, regardless of whether:

> the employee is familiar with the person and believes that he or she is healthy and disease-free; or

> the employee has done the procedure before and does not feel that there is a significant risk.

Bloodborne pathogens have been found in:

> blood
> tears
> saliva
> urine

> breast milk
> semen
> vaginal secretions
> any body fluid that is visibly contaminated with blood

OSHA has identified a list of occupations that may be associated with tasks that have occupational exposure to blood and other potentially infectious materials, as follows:

> doctors, nurses, physicians' assistants, and other employees in clinics, physicians' offices, hospitals, and other health care settings

> dentists, dental technicians, and dental hygienists

> employees of clinics, tissue banks, blood banks, medical research facilities, and diagnostic labs

CPL 02-02-069

> housekeepers in health care and other facilities

> personnel in hospital laundries or commercial laundries that service health care or public safety personnel

> employees designated to provide emergency first aid

> home health care, nursing home, and hospice employees

> staff of institutions for the developmentally disabled

> funeral home and mortuary employees

> employees of substance abuse clinics

> custodial workers who clean up contaminated sharps or spills of blood or other bodily fluids

> employees who handle regulated waste

> paramedics and other medical emergency personnel

CPL 02-02-069

> police officers, firefighters, and personnel of correctional institutions

> maintenance workers in health care facilities

> medical equipment service and repair personnel

Remember, however, that this is not a complete list. The hazard of exposure to infectious materials affects employees in many types of employment and is not restricted to the health care industry. At the same time, employees in the jobs listed above are not automatically covered UNLESS they have the potential for occupational exposure.

OSHA Letter of Interpretation — 02/01/93: Most

OSHA does not generally consider maintenance personnel and janitorial staff employed in non-health care facilities to have occupational exposure. However, it is the employer's responsibility to determine occupational exposure.

If OSHA determines that sufficient evidence of reasonably anticipated exposure exists, the employer will be held responsible for providing the protections of the Bloodborne Pathogens Standard to the employees with occupational exposure.

OSHA Letter of Interpretation — 01/26/93: Fronk

Employers in the hotel/motel industry must take into account all circumstances of potential exposure and determine which, if any, employees may come into contact with blood or other potentially infectious materials during the normal cleaning of rooms, stripping of beds, and handling of laundry from initial pick-up through laundering. Employees who handle, for example, linens soiled with urine that contains visible blood would be occupationally exposed. The employer may designate specific employees to perform the tasks and procedures, if any, that involve occupational exposure and train other employees to defer such tasks to employees designated to perform them.

Safety STOP

OSHA Letter of Interpretation — 10/19/93: Petri

Teachers are not covered by the Standard unless they are designated as responsible for rendering first-aid or medical assistance should the need arise or have other occupational exposure. If the teacher's only exposure is as a result of a designated first-aider, the vaccine may be offered following the teacher's involvement in a first-aid incident.

Exposure Control Plan

Employers with employees having occupational exposure to bloodborne pathogens must establish a written Exposure Control Plan designed to eliminate or minimize employee exposure. The plan must contain:

> exposure determination

> schedule and method of implementation for:

>> methods of compliance

>> HIV and HBV research laboratories and production facilities

>> hepatitis B vaccination and post-exposure evaluation and follow-up

>> communication of hazards to employees

>> recordkeeping

>> procedure for the evaluation of exposure incidents

>> identification of job classification and tasks involving occupational exposure to blood and other potentially infectious materials

The Exposure Control Plan also must document "commercially available and effective safer medical devices" that reduce or eliminate employee exposures, especially those involving needlesticks or other sharps, as part of the annual review. This change came about as OSHA updated its requirements to reflect the Needlestick Safety and Prevention Act. Input must also be solicited from non-managerial employees who are responsible for direct patient care, and the input must be documented in the Exposure Control Plan.

§1910.1030(c)(1)

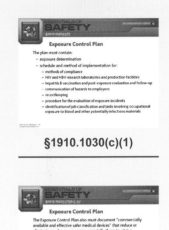

§1910.1030(c)(1)(iv), (v)

The Exposure Control Plan must be reviewed and updated at least annually and whenever necessary to reflect new or modified tasks and procedures that affect occupational exposure.

Engineering and Work Practice Controls

Engineering and work practice controls shall be used to eliminate or minimize employee exposure. Examples include:

> hand washing

> prevention of needlesticks

> minimization of the splashing or spraying of blood

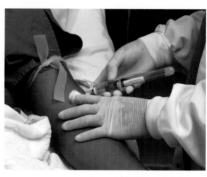

Employers must provide accessible facilities for hand washing. Hands must be washed:

> immediately after removing gloves; and

> after any hand contact with blood or potentially infectious materials.

Antiseptic cleansers must be provided if a sink is not available for hand washing. When antiseptic hand cleansers or towelettes are used, hands shall be washed with soap and running water as soon as feasible.

Employers must eliminate hazards at their source with the use of containers for used sharps that are:

> puncture-resistant;

> labeled or color-coded; and

> leakproof on the sides and bottom.

Check and maintain engineering controls on a regular schedule.

Additional engineering and work practice controls that must be used include:

> prohibiting eating, drinking, smoking, handling contact lenses, and applying cosmetics and lip balm in areas where there is a reasonable likelihood of exposure

> prohibiting storing or leaving of food or drink in areas where blood or other potentially infectious materials are present, including refrigerators, freezers, cabinets, countertops, and bench tops

> prohibiting entering work areas with contaminated garments or equipment

> packaging, labeling, and handling biohazardous waste in a way that protects employees against exposure

> prohibiting employees from engaging in mouth pipetting or suctioning of blood or other potentially infectious materials

> requiring employees to perform procedures involving blood or other potentially infectious materials in a way that minimizes splashing, spraying, spattering, and the generation of droplets

> using appropriate warning labels

> using appropriate sharps with engineered sharps injury protection

> handling contaminated laundry properly

Personal Protective Equipment

When there is occupational exposure, the employer shall provide, at no cost to the employee, appropriate personal protective equipment (PPE). PPE must be accessible and available in appropriate sizes.

Examples of PPE include:

> gloves

> gowns

> laboratory coats

> face shields or masks

> eye protection

> mouthpieces

> resuscitation bags

> pocket masks

> other ventilation devices

Housekeeping

Employers shall ensure the worksite is maintained in a clean and sanitary condition, and shall develop a written schedule for cleaning and method of decontamination within the facility.

§1910.1030(d)(2)(xii), (d)(3)(vi), (d)(4)(iii)

§1910.1030(d)(2)(xi), (d)(3)(iv), (g)(1)

§1910.1030(d)(3)

§1910.1030(d)(4)(i)

§1910.1030(b)

§1910.1030(d)(4)(iii)

Regulated Waste

Regulated waste is defined as the following types of materials:

> liquid or semi-liquid blood or other potentially infectious materials

> contaminated items that would release blood or other potentially infectious materials in a liquid or semi-liquid state if compressed

> items caked with dried blood or other potentially infectious materials that are capable of releasing these materials during handling

> contaminated sharps

> pathological and microbiological wastes containing blood or other potentially infectious materials

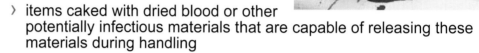

Safety STOP ™

OSHA Letter of Interpretation — 02/01/93: Most

OSHA expects products such as discarded sanitary napkins to be discarded into waste containers that are lined in such a way as to prevent contact with the contents. But at the same time, the employer must determine if employees can come into contact with blood during the normal handling of such products from initial pick-up through disposal in the outgoing trash.

Regulated waste shall be placed in containers that are:

> closable;

> constructed to contain all contents and prevent leakage of fluids;

> labeled or color-coded;

> closed prior to removal to prevent spillage; and

> disposed of in accordance with applicable federal, state, and local regulations.

Laundry

Employees must remove any garment contaminated with blood or other potentially infectious materials immediately or as soon as feasible. Laundry that is contaminated with blood or other potentially infectious materials must be:

> handled as little as possible, using gloves and any other appropriate universal precautions; and

> bagged or containerized at the location where it was used.

Laundry bags or containers generally must meet biohazard labeling and color-coding requirements. If ALL laundry is handled using universal precautions, biohazard labeling is not necessary within the facility. However, contaminated laundry must be bagged and labeled as biohazardous if it is shipped offsite to a laundry that does not use universal precautions for all laundry.

Wet contaminated laundry must be transported in bags or containers that prevent soak-through or fluid leaks.

§1910.1030(d)(4)(iv)

Hepatitis B Vaccination

This vaccination is a series of three shots made available at no cost to the employee:

> First shot — made available to all workers with an occupational exposure within 10 working days of initial assignment

> Second shot — made available one month later

> Third shot — made available 6 months later

A person has the right to refuse the hepatitis B vaccination.

See the Hepatitis B Declination Form in the Student Workbook.

Employers must also offer the vaccination as soon as possible, but in no event later than 24 hours, after exposure to infectious materials.

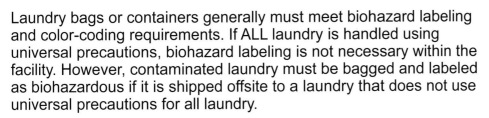

§1910.1030(f)(1), (2)

§1910.1030(b)

§1910.1030(f)(3)

§1904.8

§1910.1030(g)(1)

Exposure Incident

What is an exposure incident?

› When blood or other potentially infectious materials come into contact with a specific eye, mouth, or other mucous membrane; with non-intact skin; or when mucous membranes or the skin barrier is pierced during such events as needlesticks, human bites, cuts, and abrasions that result from the performance of an employee's duties.

What is NOT an exposure incident?

› When blood comes into contact with intact skin, meaning NO cuts, abrasions, or breaks in the skin.

Following a report of an exposure incident, the employer will arrange for an immediate confidential medical evaluation that must:

› document how the exposure occurred;

› identify and test the source individual's blood, if consent is obtained or not required;

› provide counseling; and

› evaluate, treat, and follow up on any reported illness.

The employer must provide all relevant data needed to perform an exposure evaluation.

Recording Criteria for Needlesticks

There is a recordability requirement in §1904.8:

› You must record all work-related needlestick injuries and cuts from sharp objects contaminated with another person's blood or other potentially infectious material.

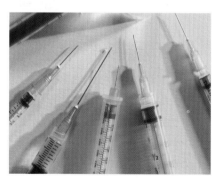

Communicate Hazards to Employees

Labels are generally required on:

› containers of regulated waste;

› specimens of blood or other potentially infectious materials;

› refrigerators and freezers containing blood or other potentially infectious materials;

› laundry bags; and

› contaminated equipment that is to be serviced or shipped.

Red bags or red containers may be substituted for labels.

For an example of the required labeling for biohazardous laundry and waste, refer the the **Example of Authorized Labeling** in your **Student Workbook.**

Training:

> Training must be provided at the time of initial assignment and at least annually thereafter.

> Provide an opportunity for interactive questions and answers.

> The training program shall contain, at a minimum, the following elements:

>> contents of the Bloodborne Pathogens Standard

>> epidemiology (the factors controlling the presence or absence of a disease or pathogen)

>> symptoms of bloodborne diseases

>> modes of transmission of bloodborne pathogens

>> Exposure Control Plan

>> methods for recognizing tasks and other activities that may involve exposures

>> use and limitations of engineering controls, work practices, and PPE

>> types, proper use, location, removal, handling, decontamination, and disposal of PPE

>> selection of PPE

>> hepatitis B vaccine

>> actions to take and persons to contact in an emergency involving bloodborne pathogens

>> procedure to follow if an exposure incident occurs

>> post-exposure evaluation and follow-up

>> signs and labels

>> opportunity for interactive question and answers with the person conducting the training session

§1910.1030(g)(2)(ii), (vii)

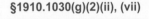

Records

Medical Record Requirements:

> The employer shall establish and maintain an accurate record for each employee with occupational exposure in accordance with 29 CFR §1910.1020.

> Keep records for at least the duration of employment plus 30 years.

§1910.1030(h)(i), (iv)

§1910.1030(h)(2)

§1910.1030(h)(5)

Training Record Requirements:

› Training records shall include the following information:

» dates of the training sessions

» contents or a summary of the training sessions

» names and qualifications of persons conducting the training

» names and job titles of all persons attending the training sessions

› Training records shall be maintained for 3 years from the date the training occurred.

Sharps Injury Log:

› The employer shall establish and maintain a sharps injury log for the recording of injuries from sharps contaminated with another person's blood.

» The event shall be recorded on the log and maintained in such manner as to protect the confidentiality of the injured employee.

» The Sharps Injury Log must contain, at a minimum:

› type and brand of device involved in the incident

› department or work area where the exposure incident occurred

› explanation of how the incident occurred

» Sharps injury logs must be kept for 5 years.

A sample Sharps Injury Log is included in the Student Workbook.

OSHA Directive – CPL 02-00-131

Employers may use the OSHA 300 Log and 301 Form to meet the Sharps Injury Log requirement of §1910.1030(h)(5) if the employer:

› Enters the type and brand of the device causing the sharps injury on the log, and

› Maintains the records in a way that segregates sharps injuries from other types of work-related injuries and illnesses, or allows sharps injuries to be easily separated

Don't forget, an injury with a sharp contaminated with another person's blood is a privacy concern case. Therefore, you may not enter the employee's name on the 300 Log. Instead, enter "privacy case" in the space normally used for the employee's name.

Module Ten

Hazard Communication, Part 1

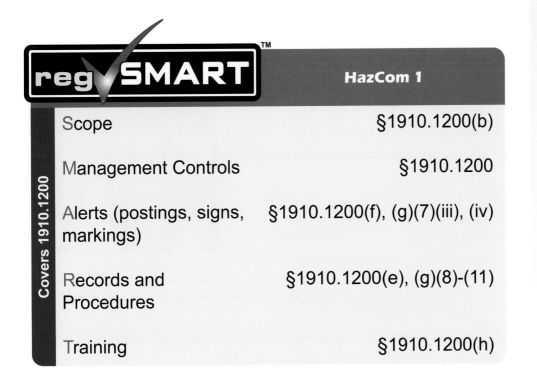

reg✓SMART™	HazCom 1
Scope	§1910.1200(b)
Management Controls	§1910.1200
Alerts (postings, signs, markings)	§1910.1200(f), (g)(7)(iii), (iv)
Records and Procedures	§1910.1200(e), (g)(8)-(11)
Training	§1910.1200(h)

Covers 1910.1200

§1910.1200(a)

§1910.1200(b)

§1910.1200(b)(6)

HazCom "The Right to Know"

Purpose

Ensure that employers and employees know about chemical hazards and how to protect themselves.

All hazard information and protective measures must be transmitted to:

› employers; and

› potentially exposed employees.

Scope and Application

This section applies to any hazardous chemical that is known to be present in the workplace in such a manner that employees may be exposed.

This section does not apply to:

› hazardous waste

› hazardous substances defined by CERCLA

› tobacco products

› wood lumber that will not be processed

» Wood or wood products that have been treated with a hazardous chemical covered by this standard and wood that may be subsequently sawed or cut, generating dust, are not exempted.

› articles, which are manufactured items other than a fluid or particles

› foods sold in a grocery store, restaurant, or drinking place and foods intended to be consumed by employees in the workplace

› drugs intended for personal consumption by employees while in the workplace (e.g., first aid supplies) and drugs in solid final form (e.g., tablets or pills) that are administered directly

› cosmetics that are packaged for sale to consumers and cosmetics intended for personal use

› nuisance particulates

› ionizing and non-ionizing radiation

› biological hazards

› consumer products where you can show that:

» they are used for the purpose intended, and

» their use is the same duration and frequency as a consumer

What Is a Hazardous Chemical?

A hazardous chemical is any chemical that is classified as a physical hazard, health hazard, simple asphyxiant, combustible dust, pyrophoric gas, or hazard not otherwise classified.

› A **physical hazard** is a chemical that is:

» explosive,

» flammable,

» an oxidizer,

» self-reactive,

» pyrophoric,

» self-heating,

» an organic peroxide,

» corrosive to metal,

» a gas under pressure, or

» emits flammable gas in contact with water.

› A **health hazard** is a chemical that poses one of the following hazardous effects:

» acute toxicity,

» skin corrosion or irritation,

» serious eye damage or irritation,

» respiratory or skin sensitization,

» germ cell mutagenicity,

» carcinogenicity,

» reproductive toxicity,

» specific target organ toxicity, or

» aspiration hazard.

› A **simple asphyxiant** is a substance or mixture that displaces oxygen in the ambient atmosphere, which can cause oxygen deprivation in those who are exposed, leading to unconsciousness or death.

§1910.1200(c)

§1910.1200(c)

§1910.1200(b)(4)

§1910.1200(e)

› A **combustible dust** can burn rapidly when in a finely divided form; if suspended in air in the right concentration, it can become explosive. Materials that may form combustible dust include metals, wood, coal, plastics, biosolids, sugar, paper, soap, dried blood, and certain textiles.

› A **pyrophoric gas** is a chemical in a gaseous state that will ignite spontaneously in air at a temperature of 130°F or below.

› A **"hazard not otherwise classified"** is a chemical that poses an adverse physical or health effect identified during the classification process that does not meet the specified criteria for the physical and health hazard classes addressed by the HazCom Standard.

Sealed Containers

When employees only handle chemicals in sealed containers that are not opened under normal conditions of use, employers must:

› ensure that incoming containers are labeled;

› maintain copies of any safety data sheets that are received with incoming shipments of the sealed containers; and

› obtain a safety data sheet as soon as possible if an employee requests the safety data sheet.

HazCom Written Program

Employers must provide a written hazard communication program for employees consisting of procedures for the following:

› **container labeling**

› **safety data sheets (SDSs):**

   » Establish a file on hazardous chemicals used in your workplace, including:

     › a copy of the latest SDSs, and

     › any other pertinent information.

› **a hazardous chemicals list:**

   » Include all hazardous chemicals present in the workplace with at least the following information:

     › manufacturer's product name listed on the SDS

     › chemical storage location

     › date first received in the workplace

› telephone number listed on the SDS

› location where the chemical is used

» Keep your list current:

› Check with your purchasing department to ensure that all hazardous chemicals purchased are included on your list.

› Read container labels to ensure these hazardous chemicals are included on your list.

› Review your list and determine whether any substances are exempt.

› **employee information and training**

› **informing employees of the hazards of:**

§1910.1200(e)

» non-routine tasks, and

» chemicals in unlabeled pipes

› **multi-employer workplaces:**

» Employers who have hazardous chemicals at a workplace where employees of another employer may be exposed must additionally ensure that procedures are established to inform the other employer of the hazards.

§1910.1200(f)

Container Labeling

The following information must appear together, in prominently displayed, legible English (although other languages may be included if appropriate), on a hazardous chemical label:

› product identifier

› signal word

› hazard statement(s)

› pictogram(s)

› precautionary statement(s)

› name, address, and telephone number of the manufacturer, importer, or other responsible party

The **"product identifier"** is the unique means by which a user can identify a hazardous chemical. It can be a name or a number. The product identifier used on the label must be the same one used on the safety data sheet.

The **"signal word"** is a word used to indicate the relative level of severity of the hazard posed by a chemical and to alert the reader. There are two signal words used:

> "Danger" is used for more severe hazards.

> "Warning" is used for less severe hazards.

A **"hazard statement"** is a statement assigned to a hazard class and category that describes the nature of the chemical's hazards including, where appropriate, the degree of hazard. An appropriate hazard statement for each hazard classification must be included on the label for products that pose more than one hazard.

Examples of hazard statements include the following (not a complete list):

> Fatal if swallowed.

> Toxic in contact with skin.

> Harmful if inhaled.

> May cause damage to organs through prolonged or repeated exposure.

> Causes severe skin burns and eye damage.

> Explosive; severe projection hazard.

> Extremely flammable material.

> Heating may cause a fire.

> May cause or intensify fire: oxidizer.

> In contact with water releases flammable gas.

> Contains gas under pressure; may explode when heated.

> May be corrosive to metals.

A **"pictogram"** is a symbol that is intended to convey specific information about the hazards of a chemical. Pictograms are in the shape of a square set at a point, with a black hazard symbol on a white background surrounded by a red frame. There are nine different pictograms that you may see on a hazardous chemical label:

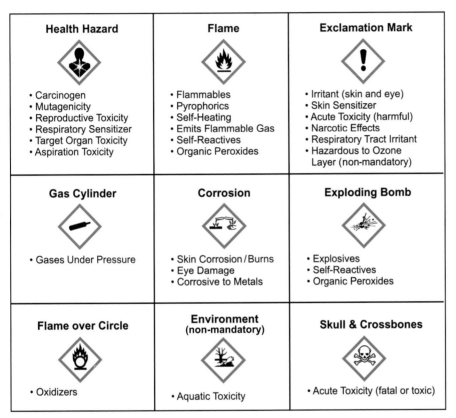

Health Hazard	Flame	Exclamation Mark
• Carcinogen • Mutagenicity • Reproductive Toxicity • Respiratory Sensitizer • Target Organ Toxicity • Aspiration Toxicity	• Flammables • Pyrophorics • Self-Heating • Emits Flammable Gas • Self-Reactives • Organic Peroxides	• Irritant (skin and eye) • Skin Sensitizer • Acute Toxicity (harmful) • Narcotic Effects • Respiratory Tract Irritant • Hazardous to Ozone Layer (non-mandatory)
Gas Cylinder	Corrosion	Exploding Bomb
• Gases Under Pressure	• Skin Corrosion/Burns • Eye Damage • Corrosive to Metals	• Explosives • Self-Reactives • Organic Peroxides
Flame over Circle	Environment (non-mandatory)	Skull & Crossbones
• Oxidizers	• Aquatic Toxicity	• Acute Toxicity (fatal or toxic)

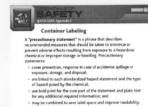

§1910.1200(c), Appendix C

A **"precautionary statement"** is a phrase that describes recommended measures that should be taken to minimize or prevent adverse effects resulting from exposure to a hazardous chemical or improper storage or handling. Precautionary statements:

> cover prevention, response in case of accidental spillage or exposure, storage, and disposal;

> are linked to each standardized hazard statement and the type of hazard posed by the chemical;

> use bold print for the core part of the statement and plain text for any additional required information; and

> may be combined to save label space and improve readability.

Container Labeling

Who is responsible for labeling containers?
- manufacturer
- importer
- distributor

Employers must make sure every container of hazardous chemicals is properly labeled. *Exceptions:*
- stationary process containers (e.g., storage tanks or other non-portable containers used in a process)
- portable containers into which hazardous chemicals are transferred from labeled containers for immediate use of the employee performing the transfer

Container Labeling

Immediate use means that the hazardous chemical will be under the control of and used only by the person who transfers it from a labeled container and only within the work shift in which it is transferred.

§1910.1200(f)(1), (7), (8)

Safety Data Sheets (SDSs)

Chemical manufacturers and importers must develop or obtain an SDS for each hazardous chemical they produce or import. Employers must have an SDS in the workplace for each hazardous chemical used.

Safety Data Sheets (SDSs)

The SDS must be in English (although copies in other languages may be maintained as well) and must contain the following section numbers, headings, and associated information in the order listed (marked to indicate no information was found, if applicable):

§1900.1200(g)

Who is responsible for labeling containers?

⟩ manufacturer

⟩ importer

⟩ distributor

Employers must make sure every container of hazardous chemicals is properly labeled. ***Exceptions:***

⟩ stationary process containers (e.g., storage tanks or other non-portable containers used in a process)

⟩ portable containers into which hazardous chemicals are transferred from labeled containers for immediate use of the employee performing the transfer

> Immediate use means that the hazardous chemical will be under the control of and used only by the person who transfers it from a labeled container and only within the work shift in which it is transferred.

Safety Data Sheets (SDSs)

Chemical manufacturers and importers must develop or obtain an SDS for each hazardous chemical they produce or import. Employers must have an SDS in the workplace for each hazardous chemical used.

The SDS must be in English (although copies in other languages may be maintained as well) and must contain the following section numbers, headings, and associated information in the order listed (marked to indicate no information was found, if applicable):

Section 1, Identification: This section lists:

⟩ the name of the chemical as it appears on the container label;

⟩ other means of identification;

⟩ recommended use of the chemical and restrictions on use;

⟩ the name, address, and telephone number of the manufacturer, importer, or other responsible party that makes the chemical; and

⟩ an emergency telephone number.

Section 2, Hazard(s) Identification: This section classifies the chemical according to its health and physical hazards. In addition to the classification of the hazard, this section will contain:

> a signal word ("Danger" or "Warning");

> hazard statement(s);

> hazard symbol/pictogram; and

> precautionary statement(s).

This section will also discuss any unclassified hazards (e.g., combustible dust or dust explosion hazard, etc.). Where an ingredient with unknown acute toxicity is used in a mixture at a concentration greater than or equal to 1%, this section will also contain a statement that X percent of the mixture consists of ingredients of unknown toxicity.

§1900.1200(g)(2)

Section 3, Composition/Information on Ingredients: This section lists:

> the chemical's name;

> the common name and synonyms of the chemical;

> the Chemical Abstracts Services (CAS) number and other unique identifiers; and

> any impurities and stabilizing additives that are themselves classified and that contribute to the classification of the substance.

For mixtures, the chemical name and concentration or concentration ranges of all ingredients that are classified as health hazards will be listed. If a trade secret is claimed for the product, this section requires a statement be made that the specific chemical identity and/or percentage of composition has been withheld as a trade secret.

Section 4, First-Aid Measures: This section describes:

> the first-aid measures that may be necessary, subdivided according to the different routes of exposure (inhalation, skin/eye contact, ingestion);

> the most important symptoms or effects of exposure, both acute and delayed; and

> any special treatment that may be required or indication of the necessity for immediate medical attention if exposure occurs.

§1910.1200(g)(2)

Section 5, Fire-Fighting Measures: This section discusses how to fight any fires that the chemical may produce or be involved in, including:

> suitable fire-extinguishing media (i.e., what type of fire extinguisher to use, etc.);

> any unsuitable fire-extinguishing media;

> the specific hazards arising from the chemical (e.g., the nature of any hazardous combustion products); and

> any special protective equipment and precautions necessary for fire fighters.

Section 6, Accidental Release Measures: This section:

> lists any personal precautions, protective equipment, and emergency procedures that are necessary; and

> describes methods and materials for containment and cleaning up of a spill.

Section 7, Handling and Storage: This section explains:

> precautions for safe handling; and

> conditions for safe storage, including information on any incompatibles.

Section 8, Exposure Controls/Personal Protection: This section:

> states the OSHA permissible exposure limit, ACGIH threshold limit value, and any other exposure limit used or recommended by the entity that prepared the SDS;

> describes any appropriate engineering controls; and

> describes any necessary individual protection measures, such as personal protective equipment.

Section 9, Physical and Chemical Properties: This section includes the following information about the chemical:

> appearance (physical state, color, etc.)

> odor

> odor threshold

> pH

> melting point and freezing point

> initial boiling point and boiling range

> flash point

> evaporation rate

> flammability

> upper and lower flammability or explosive limits

> vapor pressure

> vapor density

> relative density

> solubility

> partition coefficient (n-octanol/water)

> auto-ignition temperature

> decomposition temperature

> viscosity

§1910.1200(g)(2)

Section 10, Stability and Reactivity: This section includes the following information about the chemical:

> reactivity

> chemical stability

> possibility of hazardous reactions

> conditions to avoid (e.g., static discharge, shock, vibration, etc.)

> incompatible materials

> hazardous decomposition products

Section 11, Toxicological Information: This section describes the various toxicological (health) effects of the chemical and the available data used to identify those effects. This information will include:

> information on the likely routes of exposure (inhalation, ingestion, skin contact, eye contact, etc.);

> symptoms related to the physical, chemical, and toxicological characteristics of the chemical;

> the delayed, immediate, and chronic effects from short- and long-term exposure; and

> numerical measures of toxicity, such as acute toxicity estimates.

§1910.1200(g)(2)

§1910.1200(g)(6)

Section 12, Ecological Information: This section describes the impact the chemical has on the environment and includes information on the chemical's:

> ecotoxicity;

> persistence and degradability;

> bioaccumulative potential;

> mobility in soil; and

> any other adverse effects the chemical may have, such as posing a hazard to the ozone layer.

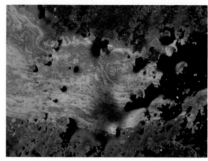

Section 13, Disposal Considerations: This section describes the chemical's waste residues. Information on the safe handling of waste residues and methods of disposal, including the disposal of any contaminated packaging, is also given in this section.

Section 14, Transport Information: This section gives the information necessary to safely and legally transport the chemical, including the chemical's:

> UN number;

> UN proper shipping name;

> transport hazard class(es);

> packaging group, if applicable;

> environmental hazards (e.g., whether the chemical is a marine pollutant, etc.);

> bulk transportation information; and

> any special precautions that a user needs to be aware of, or needs to comply with, in connection with transport or conveyance either within or outside of the user's premises.

Section 15, Regulatory Information: This section lists the safety, health, and environmental regulations for the product in question.

Section 16, Other Information: This section lists any other important information about the chemical, including the date of preparation of the SDS or the last change to it.

SDSs must be provided:

> with the first shipment of hazardous chemicals;

> with the first shipment after an SDS is updated; and

> upon an employer's request.

Employers must ensure that SDSs for every hazardous chemical onsite are readily accessible during each work shift to employees when they are in their work areas. Electronic access is permitted so long as no barriers to immediate employee access are created.

§1910.1200(g)(8)

Employee Training

Employers must inform and train employees:

> at time of initial assignment to a work area where hazardous chemicals are present; and

> whenever a new hazard is introduced into the work area.

> **Vital part of HazCom**
> Train and retrain employees.
> Keep training simple.
> Document training.

Employees must be informed of the following:

> provisions of the Hazard Communication Standard

> hazardous chemicals present in their work area

> location and availability of the written hazard communication program, including:

>> required list(s) of hazardous chemicals

>> SDSs

Employee training must include:

> ways to detect the presence or release of a hazardous chemical in the work area, such as:

>> monitoring conducted by the employer

>> continuous monitoring devices

>> characteristics of hazardous chemicals when released:

> visual appearance

> odor

§1910.1200(h)

§1910.1200(h)

Editor's Insight

› hazards of chemicals in the work area

› specific procedures the employer has implemented:

» appropriate work practices

» emergency procedures

» PPE to use

› details of the hazard communication program's explanation of:

» SDSs, including the order of information and how employees can obtain and use them,

» labels on shipped containers and workplace labeling, and

» how to obtain and use appropriate hazard information.

HazMat Labeling System

Department of Transportation

This DOT HazMat label does **not** meet OSHA HazCom labeling requirements.

HazCom requires employers to label, tag, or mark each hazardous chemical container with the product identifier, a signal word, hazard and precautionary statements, and the supplier's identification in addition to pictogram(s).

This DOT label does not contain this information.

Module Eleven

Inspections, Citations, and Penalties

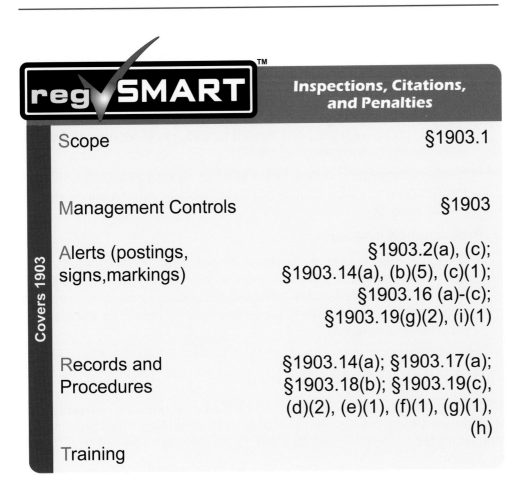

reg✓SMART™

	Inspections, Citations, and Penalties
Scope	§1903.1
Management Controls	§1903
Alerts (postings, signs,markings)	§1903.2(a), (c); §1903.14(a), (b)(5), (c)(1); §1903.16 (a)-(c); §1903.19(g)(2), (i)(1)
Records and Procedures	§1903.14(a); §1903.17(a); §1903.18(b); §1903.19(c), (d)(2), (e)(1), (f)(1), (g)(1), (h)
Training	

Covers 1903

regSMART

§1903.13; OSHA Field Operations Manual

§1904.39; OSHA Field Operations Manual

§1903.11; OSHA Field Operations Manual

§1903; OSHA Field Operations Manual

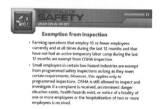

OSHA CPL 02-00-051

Reasons for Inspections

Inspection priorities are as follows:

> **Imminent Danger**

  » "Imminent danger" means conditions or practices exist that could reasonably be expected to cause immediate death or serious physical harm to employees.

> **Fatality/Catastrophe Investigations (report to OSHA within 8 hours)**

  » "Fatality" means an employee death resulting from an accident or an illness caused by or related to a workplace hazard.

  » "Catastrophe" means the hospitalization of two or more employees resulting from an accident or an illness caused by a workplace hazard.

> **Complaints/Referrals Investigations**

  » "Complaint" means a notice of an alleged hazard, or a violation of the Act, given by a past or present employee, a representative of employees, or a concerned citizen.

  » "Referral" means a notice of an alleged hazard or a violation of the Act given by any source not listed above; referrals include media reports.

> **Programmed Inspections**

  » "Programmed inspection" means inspections of worksites that have been scheduled based upon objective or neutral selection criteria. The worksites are selected according to national, regional, and local scheduling plans for safety and for health or special emphasis programs.

Exemption from Inspection

> Farming operations that employ 10 or fewer employees currently and at all times during the last 12 months and that have not had an active temporary labor camp during the last 12 months are exempt from OSHA inspection.

> Small employers in certain low-hazard industries are exempt from programmed safety inspections as long as they meet certain requirements. However, this applies only to programmed inspections. OSHA is still allowed to inspect and investigate if a complaint is received, an imminent danger situation exists, health hazards exist, or notice of a fatality of one or more employees or the hospitalization of two or more employees is received.

Employer Rights

The employer has the right to limit the inspection to only those areas identified by the inspector.

The employer has the right to deny entry into the workplace or stop the inspection at any time and request a warrant.

§1903.4

Inspection Preparation

What should you do before the OSHA compliance safety and health officer arrives?

Inspection Kit

> container for inspection kit
> paper and pens for documentation
> tape recorder for documentation
>> tapes and batteries
> camera for documentation
> flashlight for nooks and crannies
> tape measure for measurements
> noise monitoring equipment:
>> If your company does not perform monitoring, contact a subcontractor when necessary.
> air quality monitoring equipment:
>> If your company does not perform monitoring themselves, contact subcontractor when necessary.
> tote bag to carry inspection materials
> any other items that your company will need to help with inspections

Inspection Procedures

> Identify proper company officials.
> Identify designated waiting area for inspectors.
> Develop procedures for initial contact personnel to follow when the inspector arrives. This could include security or reception personnel.
>> Lead inspector to the waiting area.
>> Notify proper company officials, safety manager, etc.

Editor's Insight

> Identify the union representative.

>> If the company has a union, its representative must be permitted to be involved in the inspection.

> Discuss with supervisors the need to continue enforcing safety and health rules during an inspection.

> Don't give up just because you are being inspected!!

> Identify sources and areas of confidential and proprietary information.

> Centralize your records and know the location of all your records, such as:

>> written programs

>> 300 Log for injuries and illnesses

>> 301 Forms

>> training documents

>> inspection records

>> exposure records

>> SDSs and list of hazardous chemicals

The Inspection

Opening Conference

> **OSHA Inspector:**

>> Displays official credentials.

>> Explains why the establishment was selected for inspection.

>> Obtains information about the facility.

>> Explains the inspection procedures.

> **Employers:**

>> Should always insist on seeing the inspector's credentials.

>> Establish whether the inspector has a warrant.

>> Review the warrant.

>> Establish the purpose and scope of the inspection.

>> Determine which documents the inspector wishes to review.

Review of Records

› OSHA inspector will review injury and illness records for 5 prior calendar years.

› OSHA inspector will request copies of :

  » OSHA 300 Logs

  » total hours worked each year

  » average number of employees for each year

  » roster of current employees

› OSHA inspector will ask for the OSHA 301 Log if he or she has questions.

› OSHA inspector will check if there is an onsite medical facility and/or the location of the nearest emergency room where employees may be treated.

Walkaround Inspection

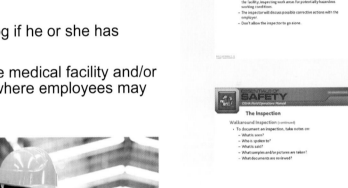

› **Walkaround procedures:**

  » The inspector and employer representative will proceed through the facility, inspecting work areas for potentially hazardous working conditions.

  » The inspector will discuss possible corrective actions with the employer.

  » Don't allow the inspector to go alone.

› **To document an inspection, take notes on:**

  » What is seen?

  » Who is spoken to?

  » What is said?

  » What samples and/or pictures are taken?

  » What documents are reviewed?

OSHA Field
Operations Manual

OSHA Field Operations Manual

Editor's Insight

§1903.16;
§1903.19(b)(2)

§1903.15; §1903.17

Closing Conference

> **OSHA inspector will:**

>> Discuss with the employer all hazardous conditions.

>> Indicate all citations that may be recommended.

>> Explain the appeal rights and procedures for contesting citations.

>> Inform the employer of obligations regarding any citations issued.

> **Employer should:**

>> Provide additional relevant information.

>> Not make admissions of guilt.

>> Not argue the case with the inspector, saving that for appeal with the area director.

>> Keep answers direct and simple; do not divulge more than necessary.

>> Request a receipt for any documents that have been provided.

If Citations Are Issued

> **Employers should:**

>> Review the citations upon receipt:

> OSHA sends citations to the employer by certified mail; hand delivery of citations to the employer or an appropriate agent of the employer may be substituted for certified mailing if it is believed that this method would be more effective.

> Therefore, any correspondence with OSHA should also be sent certified mail, and a signed receipt should be obtained and kept on file.

Note: Make sure a procedure is in place to receive and file any correspondence or documents.

>> Do the following for uncontested violations:

> Promptly post citations near the area of each violation for a minimum of 3 working days or until the citation is abated, whichever is longer.

> Remedy these violations within the stated abatement period.

» Do the following for contested violations:

› Promptly post citations near the area of each violation for a minimum of three working days or until the citation is abated, whichever is longer.

› Post a notice in the same location indicating that the citation is being contested. The notice may explain the reasons for contesting and that specified steps have been taken to abate the violation.

› Request an informal conference.

› Submit a notice of contest.

Appeal Process

Notice of Contest

› The informal conference does not stall the 15-day clock!

› A notice of contest must be submitted within 15 working days of receipt of citation notice or the notice of contest will be considered invalid.

§1903.15; §1903.17

> **If you don't submit, you cannot appeal the citation!**

Informal Conference

› **Always request an informal conference when a citation is received.**

» OSHA can clarify citations.

» Additional information may be provided.

» You can negotiate:

› penalty,

› violation, and

› abatement date.

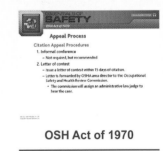

§1903.20

Citation Appeal Procedures

1. Informal conference

» Not required, but recommended

2. Letter of contest

» Issue a letter of contest within 15 days of citation.

OSH Act of 1970

OSH Act of 1970

**OSHA Field
Operations Manual**

» Letter is forwarded by OSHA area director to the Occupational Safety and Health Review Commission.

› The commission will assign an administrative law judge to hear the case.

3. Administrative law proceeding

4. Occupational Safety and Health Review Commission

5. U.S. Court of Appeals

Penalties

The maximum amount of an employer's potential fine or penalty is based on the classification of the violation, as follows:

› **De Minimis Violations ($0 per Violation):** The violation of an OSHA regulation poses no real hazard to employees because the relationship between the violation and the health and safety of employees is negligible or remote. OSHA has the discretion to issue a notice in lieu of citation. The notice carries no fine or penalty and imposes no abatement requirement.

› **Other-Than-Serious Violations (up to $12,471 per Violation):** The hazard probably would not cause death or serious physical harm, but has a direct and immediate relationship to the safety and health of employees.

› **Serious Violations (up to $12,471 per Violation):** The hazard:

» creates a substantial probability of death or serious harm, and

» was known or should have been known to the employer.

› **Posting Violations:** The violation of any posting regulations may lead to fines of up to $12,471 per violation.

› **Repeated Violations (Up to $124,709 per Violation):** The violation is substantially similar to one for which the employer was cited during a previous inspection.

› **Willful Violations ($8,908 to $124,709 per Violation):** The violation was committed with an intentional disregard for, or plain indifference to, OSHA requirements. Reckless conduct by an employer, not just deliberate wrongdoing, may lead to a finding of willfulness.

> **Willful Violations Causing Death to Employees (up to $10,000 and/or Imprisonment up to 6 Months per Violation):** The violation was committed with an intentional disregard for, or plain indifference to, OSHA requirements. Subsequent violations may receive a fine up to $20,000 and/or imprisonment up to 1 year. Violators may also face criminal penalties of imprisonment for up to 6 months (1 year for a second offense) and fines of up to $250,000 ($500,000 for an organization).

> **Giving Advance Notice of an Inspection (up to $1,000 and/or Imprisonment of up to 6 Months per Violation):** The violator gave advance notice to an employer of an OSHA inspection without authority. A fine of $3,563 may be imposed if the employer receives an authorized advance notice of inspection but fails to notify the authorized employee representative as required.

> **False Statements, Representation, or Certification (up to $10,000 and/or Imprisonment for up to 6 Months per Violation):** The violator knowingly made a false statement, representation, or certification in an application, record, report, plan, or other document filed or maintained under to the Act.

> **Failure to Abate Violations:** The failure to abate a violation within the designed period subjects the employer to fines of up to $12,471 per day for each day the violation continues. Partial abatement of a hazard may lead to reductions in fines of 25% to 75%.

> **Records Access Violation:** The failure to provide required access to employees medical and exposure records subject the employer to a fine of $1,782 for each record, up to a maximum of $12,471.

After the violation is classified, OSHA proposes a gravity-based penalty, which is then adjusted based on the business's size, good faith, and history of OSHA violations.

Notes:

> When required to provide PPE to each worker required to use it, each failure to provide required PPE to a worker may be considered a separate OSHA violation.

> Each failure to train a worker as required by an OSHA standard may be considered a separate OSHA violation.

OSHA Field Operations Manual

§1903.6(c); OSHA Field Operations Manual

§1910.9; OSHA Field Operations Manual

Notes

Module Twelve

Occupational Noise Exposure

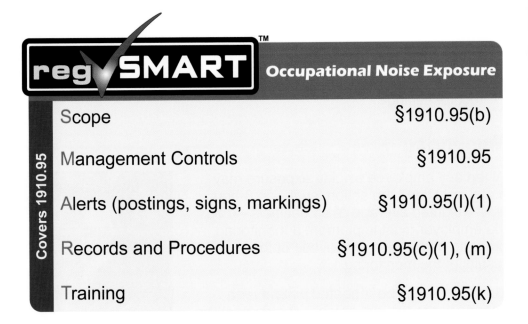

regSMART™	Occupational Noise Exposure
Scope	§1910.95(b)
Management Controls	§1910.95
Alerts (postings, signs, markings)	§1910.95(l)(1)
Records and Procedures	§1910.95(c)(1), (m)
Training	§1910.95(k)

Covers 1910.95

regSMART

§1910.95(c)(1)

§1910.95(d)

Hearing Conservation

Employers must take action to protect or conserve the hearing of their employees whenever employee exposure equals or exceeds a time-weighted, 8-hour sound level of 85 decibels (dBA). This is called the "action level."

If sound levels reach the action level, employers must administer an effective hearing conservation program that includes the following:

> monitoring

> audiometric testing

> use of hearing protectors

> training

> recordkeeping

Monitoring

When any employee's noise exposure may equal or exceed the action level—an 8-hour, time-weighted average of 85 decibels—then the employer must implement a monitoring program and inform employees of the results of the monitoring.

Monitoring must be repeated whenever a change in production, process, equipment, or controls increases noise exposures to the extent that:

> additional employees may be exposed at or above the action level; or

> the protection provided by the hearing protectors being used may no longer be sufficient.

Audiometric Testing

An audiometric test is a procedure for checking a person's hearing. If an employee's noise exposure equals or exceeds the hearing conservation action level—an 8-hour, time-weighted average of 85 decibels, calculated without regard to any reduction that may be provided by hearing protectors—then the employer must provide employees with audiometric testing.

§1910.95(g)(5), (6)

The first test is called the "baseline audiogram." This provides a "snapshot" of an employee's hearing and establishes a base to identify changes. The baseline audiogram must be made within 6 months (or 1 year, if a mobile test van is used) of first exposure at or above the action level.

§1910.95(g)(5)(i), (ii)

At least once every year after the baseline audiogram, the employee must obtain a new audiogram for each employees exposed to an 8-hour, time-weighted average of 85 decibels or higher. The annual audiogram is compared to the baseline audiogram to determine if a "standard threshold shift" has occurred.

§1910.95(g)(6)

A "standard threshold shift" is defined as an average change of 10 decibels or more in either ear at 2,000, 3,000, or 4,000 hertz (hz) relative to the baseline audiogram. An OSHA table entitled "Calculation and Applications of Age Corrections to Audiograms" may be used to consider the natural effects of aging in determining if there has been a standard threshold shift. (See §1910.95 Appendix F)

§1910.95(g)(6)

Employers must inform employees in writing within 21 days after an annual audiogram indicates that a standard threshold shift has occurred. Unless a physician determines that the standard threshold shift is not work-related, the employer must:

> immediately require the employee to use hearing protectors and train the employee in their use, if the employee is not already using such protection;

> refit the employee (with devices that offer more protection, if necessary) and retrain the employee, if the employee is already using hearing protection; and

> refer the employee for an appropriate medical evaluation.

§1910.95(g)(8)-(10)(i)

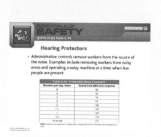

- Engineering controls
- Safe work practices
- Protective equipment

Hearing Protectors

When employees are subject to sound exceeding those listed in Table G-16, feasible administrative or engineering controls must be utilized to reduce the noise hazard.

› Engineering controls limit the production of noise. Examples include mufflers, sound barriers, sound-absorbing acoustical tile, and vibration mounts.

› Administrative controls remove workers from the source of the noise. Examples include removing workers from noisy areas and operating a noisy machine at a time when few people are present.

Table G-16 - Permissible Noise Exposures[1]	
Duration per day, hours	Sound level dBA slow response
8	90
6	92
4	95
3	97
2	100
1½	102
1	105
1/2	110
1/4 or less	115

[1] When the daily noise exposure is composed of two or more periods of noise exposure of different levels, their combined effect should be considered, rather than the individual effect of each. If the sum of the following fractions: $C_1 / T_1 + C_2 / T_2 C_n / T_n$ exceeds unity, then, the mixed exposure should be considered to exceed the limit value. C_n indicates the total time of exposure at a specified noise level, and T_n indicates the total time of exposure permitted at that level.

Note: Exposure to impulsive or impact noise should not exceed 140 dB peak soundpressure level.

If administrative and engineering controls fail to reduce sound levels below those in Table G-16, then hearing protectors must be worn to reduce sound levels.

The following employees MUST wear hearing protectors:

> any employee who is exposed to noise above designated levels for which engineering controls and work practices are insufficient protection:

>> 90 dBA for an 8-hour, time-weighted average

>> shorter periods for higher decibel levels

> any employee who is exposed to an 8-hour, time-weighted average of 85 dBA or greater and:

>> who has not had a baseline audiogram performed, or

>> who has had a baseline audiogram performed but has experienced a standard threshold shift

Remember the following about hearing protectors:

> Hearing protectors must be made available at no cost.

> Hearing protectors must be replaced as necessary.

> Employees must have the opportunity to select their hearing protection from a variety of suitable protectors.

> Employees must be trained in the use and care of the hearing protection.

> Employers must ensure a proper initial fitting and supervise the correct use of all hearing protectors.

§1910.95(b)(1), (i)(2)

§1910.95(i)(2)

§1910.95(i)(1), (3)-(5)

Effects of Noise

Informational

TM

OSHA Note

The effects of noise can be simplified into three general categories:

› Primary effects, which include noise-induced temporary threshold shift, noise-induced permanent threshold shift, acoustic trauma, and tinnitus (ringing of the ears)

› Effects on communication and performance, which may include isolation, annoyance, difficulty concentrating, absenteeism, and accidents

› Other effects, which may include stress, muscle tension, ulcers, increased blood pressure, and hypertension

Sound begins with vibrations in the air called waves. The ear changes these sound waves into nerve impulses that are interpreted by the brain.

Sound is measured by its frequency and intensity. Frequency is the pitch (high or low) of a sound. High-frequency sounds generally pose a greater threat to hearing than lower ones! Intensity is the loudness of a sound. Loudness is measured in decibels (dBA).

There are three basic kinds of noise:

› **Wide band noise** is distributed over a wide range of frequencies (e.g., the noise produced in most manufacturing settings or by operating a combustion engine).

› **Narrow band noise** is restricted to a narrow range of frequencies (e.g., noises from circular saws, fans, or planers).

› **Impulse noise** is composed of temporary "beats" that can occur in on-and-off repeating patterns (e.g., an air hammer in operation).

Training

Employers must provide training for those who are exposed to noise at or above an 8-hour time-weighted average of 85 dBA.

> Repeat training annually.

> Ensure that each employee is informed of the following:

>> effects of noise on hearing

>> purpose of hearing protectors

>> purpose of audiometric testing

Employers must also:

> make available to affected employees copies of this standard; and

> post a copy of this standard in the workplace.

Recordkeeping

The employer must maintain an accurate record of all required employee exposure measurements. Noise exposure measurement records must be retained for two years.

The employer must maintain all employee audiometric test records, which must include the following:

> name and classification of employee

> date of audiogram

> examiner's name

> date of the last calibration of the audiometer

> employee's most recent noise exposure assessment

> accurate records of the measurements of the background sound pressure levels in audiometric test rooms

Audiometric records must be maintained for the duration of the affected employee's employment.

§1910.95(k)

§1910.95(l)(1)

§1910.95(m)(1), (3)(i)

§1910.95(m)(2)

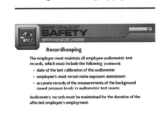

§1910.95(m)(2)(ii), (m)(3)(ii)

Notes

Module Thirteen
Personal Protective Equipment

	Personal Protective Equipment
Scope	§1910.132(a), (g); §1910.133(a)(1); §1910.135(a); §1910.136(a); §1910.138(a); §1910.140(a);
Management Controls	§1910.132; §1910.133; §1910.135; §1910.136; §1910.138; §1910.140
Alerts (postings, signs, markings)	§1910.133(a)(4), (b); §1910.135(b), §1910.136(b)
Records and Procedures	§1910.132(d), (f)(4)
Training	§1910.132(f)(1)-(3)

Covers §§1910.132; .133; .135; .136; .138

regSMART

§1910.132(a), (c), (e)

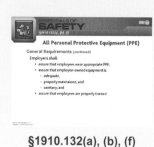

§1910.132(a), (b), (f)

§1910.132(h)

All Personal Protective Equipment (PPE)

General Requirements

PPE shall:

› be provided, used, and maintained in a sanitary and reliable condition;

› be of a safe design and construction for the work to be performed; and

› not be used if it is defective or damaged.

Employers shall:

› assure that employees wear appropriate PPE;

› assure that employee-owned equipment is:

» adequate,

» properly maintained, and

» sanitary; and

› assure that employees are properly trained.

Payment for PPE

Required PPE must be provided by the employer at no cost to employees. The employer is not required to purchase:

› non-specialty safety-toe protective footwear, including steel-toe shoes or boots;

› logging boots;

› non-specialty prescription eyewear;

› everyday clothing;

› shoes or boots with built-in metatarsal protection, when the employer provides metatarsal guards and is allowing the employee, at the employee's own request, to wear the footwear with built-in protection;

› ordinary clothing or other items for protection from the weather;

› employee-owned equipment, this is adequate PPE that an employee has decided to provide themselves; or

› replacement PPE when an employee has lost or intentionally damaged his or her PPE. (All other replacement PPE must be paid for by the employer.)

Limits of PPE

You are responsible for wearing your PPE as instructed. If you wear your assigned PPE properly, you should be protected from identified hazards. However, no PPE is perfect or incapable of failure, so it is important to recognize its limitations.

Your PPE may fail to protect you if:

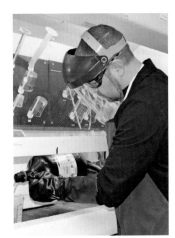

> It is improperly used.

> It is improperly fitted.

> It is poorly maintained.

> It is defective.

> It is improperly selected.

> It is incorrectly stored.

> You get careless while wearing it.

Remember, **PPE will not make you "bullet-proof" or invincible**. It should never be an excuse for slipshod safety practices.

Hazard Assessment

Employers shall assess the workplace to determine if hazards are present or likely to be present. If so, the employer must:

> select and have each affected employee use PPE;

> communicate PPE selection decisions to workers; and

> select PPE that properly fits each affected employee.

Employers can use assessment tools, such as:

> OSHA 300 Log and 301 Form

> first-aid log

> walk-through

The employer shall verify the required workplace hazard assessment has been performed through a written certification that identifies:

> workplace evaluated;

> name of the person certifying that the evaluation has been performed;

> date(s) of the hazard assessment; and

> document as a certification of hazard assessment.

Editor's Insight

§1910.132(d)(1)

Editor's Insight

§1910.132(d)(2)

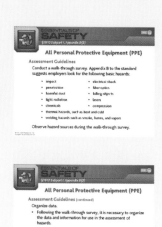

§1910 Subpart I,
Appendix B(3)

§1910 Subpart I,
Appendix B(1)

Assessment Guidelines

Conduct a walk-through survey. Appendix B to the standard suggests employers look for the following basic hazards:

> impact
> penetration
> harmful dust
> light radiation
> chemicals
> thermal hazards, such as heat and cold
> welding hazards such as smoke, fumes, and vapors

> electrical shock
> fiber optics
> falling objects
> lasers
> compression

Observe hazard sources during the walk-through survey.

Organize data.

> Following the walk-through survey, it is necessary to organize the data and information for use in the assessment of hazards.
> The objective is to prepare for an analysis of the hazards in the environment to enable proper selection of protective equipment.

Analyze data.

> Having gathered and organized data on a workplace, an estimate of the potential for injuries should be made.
> Each of the basic hazards should be reviewed and a determination made as to the type, level of risk, and seriousness of potential injury from each of the hazards found in the area.
> The possibility of exposure to several hazards simultaneously should be considered.

Personal protective equipment should be the last line of defense against work hazards. ALWAYS try to first eliminate the hazard through engineering controls and safe work practices.

See the "PPE for Workers Checklist" and the "Certification of Hazard Assessment" found in the Student Workbook for more assistance in performing the hazard assessment and selecting appropriate PPE.

Training

The employer shall provide training to those who are required to use PPE. They must know:

> when PPE is necessary;

> what PPE is necessary;

> how to properly put on, take off, adjust, and wear PPE;

> limitations of the PPE; and

> proper care, maintenance, useful life, and disposal of the PPE.

Affected employees must demonstrate understanding of the training before they are allowed to begin working with the PPE.

The employer shall retrain employees when there are:

> changes in the workplace;

> changes in the type of PPE used; or

> inadequacies in employee's knowledge.

Note: See the "Care, Maintenance, and Disposal of PPE" handout in the Student Workbook for more information on the proper care, maintenance, useful life, and disposal of required PPE.

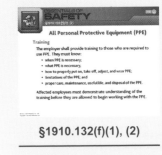

§1910.132(f)(1), (2)

§1910.132(f)(3)

Eye and Face Protection

Generally

Employees must use appropriate protection when exposed to eye or face hazards.

> Use eye protection that provides side protection where there is a hazard from flying objects.

> If requirements are met, clip-on or slide-on side shields are acceptable.

Eye and face protection must meet the following minimum requirements:

> It must provide adequate protection against particular hazards, such as flying particles, molten metal, liquid chemicals, acids or caustic liquids, chemical gases or vapors, or potentially injurious light radiation.

> It must be reasonably comfortable when worn under the designated conditions.

> It must fit snugly without interfering with the movement or vision of the wearer.

§1910.132(a)(1), (2)

§1910.133; ANSI Z89.1

Eye and Face Protection

Generally (continued)

Eye and face protection must be:
- durable;
- capable of being disinfected;
- easily cleanable;
- kept clean;
- in good repair; and
- distinctly marked to facilitate identification of the manufacturer

Safety glasses or goggles must meet the requirements of ANSI standard Z87.1 (either the 2010, 2003, or the 1998 revision of the 1989 version).

§1910.133; ANSI Z89.1

Eye and Face Protection

Prescription Lenses

If you wear prescription lenses, it is required that you wear eye protection that:
- incorporates the prescription in its design; or
- fits over your regular glasses without disturbing their proper position.

Under the ANSI standard, glasses must be able to withstand the impact of a 1-inch steel ball dropped onto the glasses from a height of 50 inches.

§1910.133(a)(3); ANSI Z89.1

Eye and Face Protection

OSHA Fact

Safety Stop

Eye and face protection must be:

> durable;

> capable of being disinfected;

> easily cleanable;

> kept clean;

> in good repair; and

> distinctly marked to facilitate identification of the manufacturer

Safety glasses or goggles must meet the requirements of ANSI standard Z87.1 (either the 2010, 2003, or the 1998 revision of the 1989 version).

Prescription Lenses

If you wear prescription lenses, it is required that you wear eye protection that:

> incorporates the prescription in its design; or

> fits over your regular glasses without disturbing their proper position.

Under the ANSI standard, glasses must be able to withstand the impact of a 1-inch steel ball dropped onto the glasses from a height of 50 inches.

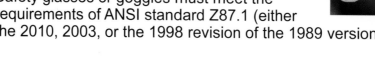

Safety STOP™

OSHA Fact

Every day, an estimated 1,000 eye injuries occur in American workplaces. The financial cost of these injuries is enormous—more than $300 million per year in lost production time, medical expenses, and workers compensation.
- The U.S. Bureau of Labor Statistics reports that almost 70% of the accidents studied resulted from flying or falling objects or sparks striking the eye.
- Contact with chemicals caused 20% of the injuries.
- Approximately 10% of the injuries were caused by objects swinging from a fixed or attached position, like tree limbs, ropes, chains, or tools that were pulled into the eye while the worker was using them.
- The U.S. Bureau of Labor Statistics also reported that nearly 60% of workers injured were not wearing eye protection at the time of the accident.

Head Protection

General Requirements

A protective helmet is required when working in areas where there is a potential for injury to the head from falling objects or to reduce electrical shock hazards when near exposed electrical conductors that could contact the head.

Head protection must:

> fit properly;

> be inspected and maintained as needed; and

> comply with ANSI Z89.1 (either 2009, 2003, or 1997), or be at least as effective.

§1910.135; ANSI Z89.1

Foot Protection

General Requirements

Use protective footwear when working in areas where there is a danger of foot injuries due to:

> falling or rolling objects

> objects piercing the sole

> exposed to electrical hazards

Foot protection must meet the requirements of one of the following consensus standards, or be at least as effective:

> ASTM F-2412-2005 and ASTM F-2413-2005

> ANSI Z41-1999

> ANSI Z41-1991

§1910.136

ANSI Z89.1

§1910.138(a)

§1910.138(b)

Under these consensus standards:

> Employers must evaluate the workplace to make sure safety shoes are suitable for the hazards in the work environment.

> Toe caps must pass a drop test where a 50-pound steel weight is dropped from a designated height at a designated speed, as follows:

Toe Cap Rating (ANSI Z41.1-1991)			
Class	Impact	50 lb. Drop Test	Compression
30	30 ft-lbs	7½ in high	1,000 lbs
50	50 ft-lbs	12 in high	1,750 lbs
75	75 ft-lbs	18 in high	2,500 lbs

Hand Protection

General Requirements

Employers must require employees to use appropriate hand protection when employees' hands are exposed to hazards such as:

> skin absorption of harmful substances

> severe cuts or lacerations

> severe abrasions

> punctures

> chemical burns

> thermal burns, and

> harmful temperature extremes

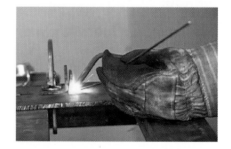

Appropriate hand protection must be selected based on:

> an evaluation of the tasks to be performed;

> the conditions present;

> the duration of use; and

> all actual and potential hazards.

Be careful around rotating machinery! Gloves may catch in moving parts.

Respiratory Protection

Respiratory Protection Program

The employer must develop and implement a written respiratory protection program.

> It must have required worksite-specific procedures and elements for required respirator use.

> The program must be administered by a suitably trained program administrator.

> Certain program elements may be required for voluntary use to prevent potential hazards associated with the use of the respirator.

§1910.134(c)

The respiratory protection program must include:

> procedures for selecting respirators

> provisions for medical evaluations of employees

> fit testing procedures

> procedures for proper use

> procedures and schedules for respirator:

>> cleaning,

>> disinfecting,

>> storing,

>> inspecting,

>> repairing,

>> discarding, and

>> maintenance.

§1910.134(c)(1)

> procedures to ensure adequate air quality, quantity, and flow of breathing air:

>> SCBA (self-contained breathing apparatus)

>> SARs (supplied-air respirators)

> training of employees in the respiratory hazards to which they are potentially exposed

> a procedure to evaluate the program regularly

§1910.134(c)(2)

§1910.134(d)(1), (3)(i)[A]

Where respirator use is not required:

> An employer may provide respirators at the request of employees or permit employees to use their own respirators.

>> The employer must determine that such respirator use will not in itself create a hazard.

> The employer shall provide the voluntary respirator users with the information contained in Appendix D of §1910.134. **(See the Student Workbook for a copy of Appendix D)**

> The employer must establish and implement elements of a written respiratory protection program necessary to ensure:

>> any employee using a respirator voluntarily is medically able to use that respirator, and

>> the respirator is cleaned, stored, and maintained so its use does not present a health hazard to the user.

Exception: A filtering facepiece, often referred to as a dust mask:

> Employers are not required to include in a written respiratory protection program those employees whose only use of respirators involves the voluntary use of filtering face-pieces.

Respirator Selection

There are two basic classes of respirators:

> air-purifying, which generally use some kind of filter or cartridge; and

> air-supplying, which actually supply air to the user.

There are two respirator fit types:

> tight-fitting (quarter masks, half masks, and full facepiece); and

> loose-fitting (hoods, helmets, blouses, or full suits that cover the head completely).

Employers must:

> select a respirator based on:

>> respiratory hazards to which the worker is exposed to, and

>> workplace and user factors that affecting respirator performance and reliability;

> select a NIOSH-certified respirator;

> identify the respiratory hazards in the workplace including:

>> a reasonable estimate of employee exposures to respiratory hazards, and

>> identification of the contaminant's chemical state and physical form;

> select respirators from a sufficient number of respirator models; and

> use the assigned protection factors (APFs) listed in §1910.134 Table 1 to select a respirator that provides proper protection.

>> "Assigned protection factor" is the level of respiratory protection that a class of respirators is expected to provide.

§1910.134(d)(1), (3)(i)[A]

Respirator Selection in **IDLH Atmospheres**

> An atmosphere that poses an immediate threat to life, would cause an irreversible adverse health effect, or would impair an individual's ability to escape from a dangerous atmosphere is called "immediately dangerous to life and health" or "IDLH." All oxygen-deficient atmospheres must be considered IDLH.

> For IDLH atmospheres, the employer must provide either:

>> a full facepiece pressure-demand self-contained breathing apparatus (SCBA) certified by NIOSHA for a minimum service life of thirty minutes; or

>> a combination full facepiece pressure-demand supplied-air respirator (SAR) with an auxiliary self-contained air supply.

> Respirators provided only for escape from IDLH atmospheres must be NIOSH-certified for escape from the atmosphere in which they will be used.

§1910.134(d)(2)

Medical Status

Medical Evaluation Procedures

> The employer shall identify a physician or other licensed health care professional (PLHCP) to perform medical evaluations using a medical questionnaire or an initial medical examination that obtains the same information as the medical questionnaire.

> Employers or supervisors are not to look at or review evaluations.

> The employer will inform employees how to deliver or send the medical evaluation questionnaire to the health care professional who will review them.

§1910.134(e)(2)

§1910.134(e)(3)

§1910.134(e)(6)

§1910.134(e)(7)

§1910.134(f)(1)

Follow-up Medical Examination

> Employers shall ensure that a follow-up medical examination is provided for employees:

» who give a positive response to any question among numbers 1 through 8 in Section 2, Part A, of the question-naire; or

» whose initial medical examination demonstrates the need for one.

Medical Determination

> **See the "Medical Determination for Respirator Use" handout in the Student Workbook.**

> In determining the employee's ability to use a respirator, the employer shall obtain a written recommendation regarding the employee's ability to use the respirator from the physician or other licensed health care professional (PLHCP), providing:

» any limitations on respirator use;

» the need, if any, for follow-up medical evaluations; and

» a statement that the PLHCP has provided the employee with a copy of the PLHCP's written recommendation.

Medical Status Reevaluation

> Additional medical evaluations shall be provided if:

» the employee reports medical signs or symptoms which relates to the ability to use a respirator;

» a PLHCP, supervisor, or the respirator program administrator informs the employer the employee needs to be reevaluated; or

» a change occurs in workplace conditions that may affect the employees' physiological burdens.

Fit Test

Administer the fit test using either of the following OSHA-accepted fit test protocols:

> Qualitative fit test (QLFT):

» A pass/fail fit test to assess the adequacy of respirator fit that relies on the person's response to the test agent.

> Quantitative fit test (QNFT):

» An assessment of the adequacy of respirator fit by numerically measuring the amount of leakage into the respirator.

Fit testing is performed:

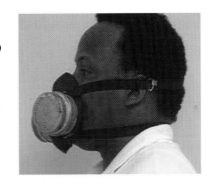

> before an employee may be required to use any respirator with a negative- or positive-pressure tight-fitting facepiece; and

> with the same make, model, style, and size of respirator that will be used.

The employee must be fit tested:

> prior to initial use of the respirator;

> whenever a different respirator facepiece (size, style, model, or make) is used; and

> at least annually thereafter.

OSHA Fact — §1910.134 Appendix A

General Fit Testing Procedure
> The test subject will pick a respirator from a sufficient number of respirators (offer a choice of style and size).
> The test subject is shown how to put on a respirator, position it on the face, set strap tension and determine an acceptable fit.
> The test subject will conduct a user seal check.
> Do not conduct the fit test if any hair growth interferes with the facepiece sealing surface.
> If a test subject exhibits difficulty breathing, refer to a physician.
> Perform the test exercises for all fit testing methods, except for the Controlled Negative Pressure (CNP) and the CNP REDON quantitative fit testing protocol (they have their own test exercises).

§1910.134(f)(2)

Safety Stop

User Seal Checks

> Employees using tight-fitting respirators must perform a user seal check each time they put on the respirator. There are two basic tests (or use manufacturer's procedures if equally effective):

>> **Positive Pressure Test:** Close the exhalation valves and breathe out gently into the facepiece, which should make it bulge slightly. If you don't hear or feel any air leaking out, you have a good fit.

>> **Negative Pressure Test:** Close the inhalation valves and breathe in gently, which should make the facepiece collapse slightly against your face. Hold your breath for 10 seconds. If the facepiece stays collapsed and no air leaks in, you have a good fit.

§1910.134; Appendix B-1

Note: See the Student Workbook for a handout on User Seal Checks.

§1910.134(g)(1)

§1910.134(h)

§1910.134(i)

§1910.134(k)

Care and Use of Respirators

Facepiece Seal Protection

> The employer shall not permit respirators with tight-fitting facepieces to be worn by employees who have any condition that interferes with face-to-facepiece seal or valve function, including facial hair that comes between the sealing surface of the facepiece and the face or that interferes with valve function.

> Make certain corrective glasses, goggles, or other personal protective equipment does not interfere with the facepiece seal.

> Make certain the user performs a seal check each time when putting on a respirator.

Maintenance and Care of Respirators

> Employers must provide for the cleaning, disinfecting, storage, inspection, and repair of respirators used by employees.

Identification of Filters, Cartridges, and Canisters

> Ensure that all filters, cartridges, and canisters used in the workplace are labeled and color-coded with the NIOSH-approval label and that the label is not removed and remains legible.

Training

Employers must provide effective training to employees who are qualified to use respirators. The training must be:

> comprehensive;

> understandable;

> performed annually; and

> performed more often if necessary.

Each employee must be able to demonstrate knowledge of at least the following:

> why the respirator is necessary and how improper fit, usage, or maintenance can compromise the protective effect of the respirator

> what the limitations and capabilities of the respirator are

> what the procedures are for maintenance and storage of the respirator

> how to use the respirator effectively in emergency situations, including situations in which the respirator malfunctions

> how to inspect, put, on, remove, use, and check the seals of the respirator

> how to recognize medical signs and symptoms that may limit or prevent the effective use of respirators

> general requirements of the Respiratory Protection Standard

§1910.134(k)

Recordkeeping

Medical Evaluation

> The required medical evaluation must be retained and made available in accordance with §1910.1020.

Fit Testing

> Employers must establish a record of the qualitative and quantitative fit tests that includes:

» name or identification of the employee tested;

» type of fit test performed;

» specific make, model, style, and size of respirator tested;

» date of test; and

» pass/fail results for qualitative fit tests or the fit factor and strip chart recording or other recording of the test results for quantitative fit tests.

§1910.134(m)(1), (2)

Fit test records shall be retained for respirator users until the next fit test.

A written copy of the current respirator program shall be retained by the employer.

§1910.134(m)(1)-(3)

Mandatory Appendices

A: Fit Testing Procedures

B-1: User Seal Check Procedures

B-2: Respirator Cleaning Procedures

C: OSHA Respirator Medical Evaluation Questionnaire

D: Information for Employees Using Respirators When Not Required Under the Standard.

§1910.134

Personal Fall Protection

A **personal fall protection system** is a system, including all components, used to provide protection from falling or to safely arrest a fall if one occurs. Examples of personal fall protection systems include:

> personal fall arrest systems (PFASs), which are used to arrest a user's fall from a walking-working surface

> positioning systems, which allow the user to be supported on an elevated vertical surface, such as a wall or window sill, and work with both hands free

> travel restraint systems, which are used to eliminate the possibility of the user going over the edge of a walking-working surface

If fall protection is required and a personal fall protection system will be used to meet that requirement, then the fall protection system must meet these requirements (not a complete list):

> **Use:** Personal fall protection systems and their components must be used exclusively for employee fall protection and not for any other purpose such as hoisting equipment or materials.

> **Impact Loading:** A personal fall protection system or any of its components that is subject to impact loading must be immediately removed from service and not used again until a competent person inspects the system or component and determines that it is not damaged and is safe for use as employee fall protection.

> **Inspection:** Systems must be inspected before initial use during each work shift for mildew, wear, damage, and other deterioration; defective components must be removed from service.

> **Component Protection:** Ropes, belts, lanyards, lifelines, and harnesses used for personal fall protection must be protected from being cut, abraded, melted, or otherwise damaged.

> **Rescue:** The employer must provide for prompt rescue of each employee in the event of a fall.

> **Positions for Use:** Systems must be worn with the attachment point of the body harness located in the center of the employee's back near shoulder level. If the free fall distance is limited to 2 feet or less, the attachment point may be located in the pre-sternal position.

§1910.140(b)

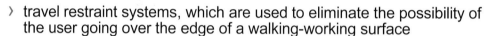

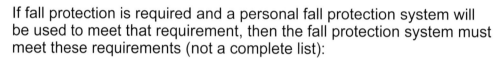

§§1910.29(j); 1910.140(b)

> **Lifelines:** When vertical lifelines are used, each employee must be attached to a separate lifeline. Lifelines may not be made of natural rope fiber.

> **Snaphooks and Carabiners:** Snaphooks and carabiners must lock automatically and require at least two separate, consecutive movements to open. Unless designed for such use, they may not be connected:

>> directly to webbing, rope, or wire rope,

>> to each other,

>> to a D-ring to which another snaphook, carabiner, or connector is attached,

>> to a horizontal lifeline, or

>> to any object that is incompatibly shaped or dimensioned such that disengagement could occur when the connected object depresses the snaphook or carabiner gate and allows the components to separate.

> **Anchorages:** Anchorages used to attach personal fall protection equipment must be:

>> independent of any anchorage used to suspend employees or platforms on which employees work,

>> attached to an overhead member of the platform, at a point located above and near the center of the platform, if used to attach to personal fall protection equipment on mobile work platforms on powered industrial trucks, and

>> capable of supporting at least 5,000 pounds for each employee attached or designed, installed, and used under the supervision of a qualified person as part of a complete fall protection system that maintains a safety factor of at least two.

> **Manufacturer's Recommendations:** Equipment must be cared for, inspected, stored, and used as recommended by the manufacturer.

> **PFASs:** PFASs must:

>> limit the maximum arresting force on the user to 1,800 pounds,

>> bring the user to a stop and limit the maximum deceleration distance traveled to 3.5 feet,

>> be rigged so that an employee cannot free fall more than 6 feet or contact a lower level, and

>> not use body belts as part of the system.

§1910.140(c)

§1910.140(c), (d)(1), (d)(2)

> **Positioning Systems:** Positioning systems must be capable of withstanding without failure a drop test consisting of a 4-foot drop of a 250-pound weight.

> **Window Cleaners' Positioning Systems:** Window cleaners' positioning systems must:

  » be strong enough to withstand a 6-foot drop of a 250-pound weight,

  » limit the initial arresting force on a falling employee to not more than 2,000 pounds, with a duration not exceeding 2 milliseconds and any subsequent arresting forces to not more than 1,000 pounds,

  » have belts with runners that are 8 feet or less and terminals that will not pass through their fastenings if a terminal comes loose form the window anchor,

  » have window anchors to which belts are fastened installed 42 – 51 inches above the window sill,

  » have window anchors capable of supporting a minimum load of 6,000 pounds,

  » have both terminals of the window cleaner's belt attached to separate window anchors during any cleaning operation,

  » not be used if the window sill/ledge has snow or ice or is otherwise slippery, weakened, or rotted,

  » not be used on sills/ledges that are less than 4 inches wide or that slope more than 15° below horizontal (*Exception*: The 4-inch minimum is increased 0.4 inches for every degree the sill/ledge slopes beyond 15°, up to a maximum of 30°.),

  » be used so that employees attach at least one belt terminal to a window anchor before climbing through the window opening, keeping at least one terminal attached until completely back inside the window opening, and

  » generally be used so that employees traveling from one window to another return inside the window opening and repeating the belt terminal attachment procedure at each window.

> **Lineman's Body Belt and Pole Strap Systems:** See 29 CFR 1910.140(e)(iv) for requirements.

Module Fourteen

Permit-Required Confined Spaces, Part 1

regSMART™	Permit-Required Confined Spaces
Scope	§1910.146(a); §1926.21(b)(6)(ii)
Management Controls	§1910.146
Alerts (postings, signs, markings)	§1910.146(c)(2)
Records and Procedures	§1910.146(c)(5)(ii)[H], (c)(7)(iii), (d)-(f), (g)(4), (k)(2)(iii)
Training	§1910.146(g)-(j), (k)(2)

Covers 1910.146

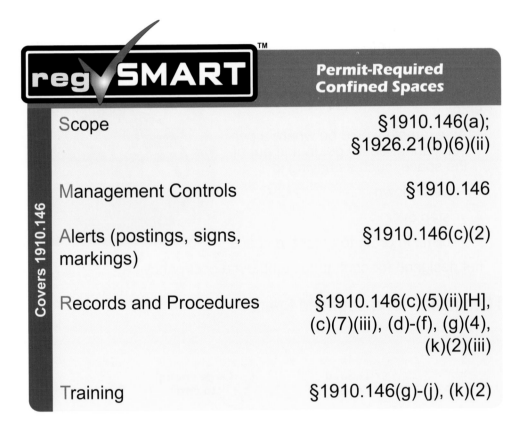

Confined Spaces

A confined space has the following three characteristics:

› large enough and so configured that an employee can bodily enter and perform assigned work

  » An example of an opening that is large enough to enter may be a floor, platform, pavement, or yard opening that is 12 inches or more in its least dimension in which people may fall, such as:

    › a hatchway

    › a stairway or ladder opening

    › a pit

    › a large manhole

› limited or restricted in its means for entry

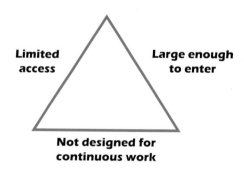

  » An example would be where a person cannot easily get in and out of the space, such as having to:

    › bend down

    › step over

    › climb in or up to enter the space

› not designed for continuous employee occupancy

3 Conditions for a Confined Space

Limited access

Large enough to enter

Not designed for continuous work

Your space is not a confined space if it does not meet these three conditions.

Types of confined spaces:

> crawl spaces
> attics
> manholes
> storage tanks
> pits
> vats
> vessels
> silos
> hoppers
> vaults

Permit-Required Confined Spaces

A permit-required confined space is a confined space that has one or more of the following characteristics:

> contains or has a potential to contain a hazardous atmosphere
> contains a material that has the potential for engulfing an entrant
> has an internal configuration that could trap or asphyxiate an entrant
> contains any other recognized serious safety or health hazard

4 Conditions for a Permit-Required Confined Space

Limited access — Large enough to enter — Contains a hazard — Not designed for continuous work

A permit-required confined space is a confined space that contains a serious safety or health hazard.

§1910.146(c)(1), (2)

§1910.146(c)(3),
(c)(4), (d)(1)-(3)

§1910.146(d)(4)-(6), (8)

§1910.146(d)(9), (11), (14)

General Requirements

› Evaluate the workplace to determine if any spaces are permit required confined spaces. **Refer to the "Permit-Required Space Decision Flow Chart" in your Student Workbook for assistance in making this determination.**

» Inform exposed employees by posting danger signs or using any other equally effective means:

"DANGER PERMIT- REQUIRED CONFINED SPACE, DO NOT ENTER"

» Develop and implement a written permit space program and include a permit system.

› Implement the measures necessary to prevent unauthorized entry.

› Identify and evaluate the hazards of permit spaces before employees enter them.

› Develop and implement the means, procedures, and practices necessary for safe permit space entry operations.

› Provide, maintain, and ensure that employees use any necessary testing/monitoring, ventilating, communications, personal protective equipment, etc.

› Provide at least one attendant outside the permit space when entry operations are being conducted.

› Identify those with active roles and their duties, and provide training.

› Develop and implement procedures for rescue and emergency services.

› Coordinate entry operations when there are multiple employers.

› Perform an annual review of the program.

Contractors

› When an employer arranges to have employees of a contractor perform work that involves permit space entry:

» Inform the contractor that permit space entry is allowed only through compliance with a permit space program.

» Apprise the contractor of the hazards identified.

» Apprise the contractor of any precautions or procedures the host employer has implemented.

» Coordinate entry operations with the contractor.

» Debrief the contractor at the conclusion of the entry operations.

Permit System

› Before entry is authorized:

» Document the following measures by preparing an entry permit:

› Specify acceptable entry conditions.

› Provide affected employees the opportunity to observe any monitoring or testing.

› Isolate the permit space.

› Eliminate or control atmospheric hazards.

› Provide barriers as necessary to protect entrants from external hazards.

› Verify that conditions are acceptable for entry throughout the duration of an authorized entry.

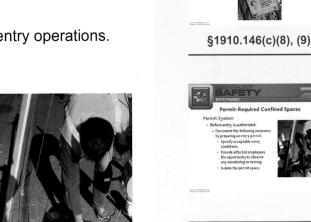

§1910.146(c)(8), (9)

§1910.146(d)(3)

§1910.146(e)(2)

§1910.146(e)(6)

§1910.146(g)(1), (2)

§1910.146(g)(4)

> Before entry begins:

>> The entry supervisor identified on the permit shall sign the entry permit to authorize entry.

> After entry is completed:

>> Retain each canceled entry permit for at least 1 year to assist with the review of the permit-required confined space program.

>> Any problems encountered during an entry operation shall be noted on the pertinent permit so that appropriate revisions to the permit space program can be made.

Training

Provide training so that all employees acquire necessary understanding, knowledge, and skills for the safe performance of their duties.

Training shall be provided to each affected employee:

> before the employee is first assigned duties;

> before there is a change in assigned duties;

> when there is a change in permit space operations;

> when there are deviations from the permit space entry procedures; and

> when there are inadequacies in the employee's knowledge.

To certify that the training has been accomplished, the certification shall contain:

> each employee's name;

> signatures or initials of the trainers; and

> dates of training.

Duties of the Authorized Entrant

> The authorized entrant must do the following:

  » Know the hazards that may be faced, including information on the mode, signs or symptoms, and consequences of exposure.

  » Know the mode of exposure (e.g., inhalation, skin, etc.), signs/ symptoms of exposure, and consequences of exposure.

  » Use equipment properly.

  » Know what the evacuation alarm sounds or looks like.

  » Communicate with attendant at all times.

  » Alert the attendant when:

    > a warning sign or symptom of exposure is recognized, or

    > a prohibited condition is detected.

  » Exit as quickly as possible whenever:

    > an order to evacuate is given by the attendant or entry supervisor,

    > warning signs or symptoms of exposure are recognized,

    > a prohibited condition is detected, or

    > the evacuation alarm is activated.

Refer to the "Safe Entry Checklist" in your Student Workbook for assistance in evaluating a confined space before entering it.

§1910.146(h)

§1910.146(i)

Duties of Attendants

> An attendant must do the following:

  » Know the hazards that may be faced, including information on the mode, signs or symptoms (including behavioral effects), and consequences of exposure.

  » Be aware of possible behavioral effects.

  » Maintain a continuous accurate count of authorized entrants in the permit space.

» Remain outside the permit space until relieved by another attendant.

» Communicate with authorized entrants.

» Monitor activities inside and outside the space and order the authorized entrants to evacuate the permit space immediately when the attendant detects any of the following conditions:

› a prohibited condition in or around the space

› a behavioral change in the entrant

› a situation that could be dangerous outside the space

› the attendant no longer can effectively and safely perform all of the duties required.

» Summon rescue and other emergency services as soon as the attendant determines that authorized entrants may need assistance.

» Perform non-entry rescues.

» Perform no duties that might interfere with the attendant's primary duty to monitor and protect the authorized entrants.

» Take the following actions when unauthorized persons approach or enter a permit space.

› Warn the unauthorized persons that they must stay away from the permit space.

› Advise the unauthorized persons that they must exit immediately if they have entered the permit space.

› Inform the authorized entrants and the entry supervisor if unauthorized persons have entered the permit space.

Duties of Entry Supervisor

› An entry supervisor must do the following:

» Know the hazards that may be faced, including information on the mode, signs or symptoms, and consequences of exposure.

» Verify appropriate entries have been made to the permit.

» Make sure all tests specified by the permit have been conducted.

» Verify all procedures and equipment specified by the permit are in place before allowing entry.

» Terminate the entry and cancel the permit when the conditions in the space change or when the work has been completed and verified.

» Verify that rescue services are available.

» Remove unauthorized individuals.

Rescue and Emergency Services

Designated employees on the confined space rescue team must be trained:

› as an authorized entrant;

› to perform assigned rescue duties;

› in basic first aid and cardiopulmonary resuscitation (CPR);

› on necessary PPE; and

› on practicing hands-on rescue operations by removing dummies, mannikins, or persons from actual or simulated permit spaces at least once every 12 months.

Note: If an injured entrant is exposed to a substance for which a Safety Data Sheet (SDS) is kept at the worksite, make it available to the medical facility treating the exposed entrant.

§1910.146(j)

§1910.146(k)

§1910.146(k)(3)

Retrieval Systems

Each authorized entrant must use:

> a chest or full body harness; and

> a retrieval line that is:

>> attached at the center of the entrant's back, near shoulder level, above the entrant's head, and

>> attached at the other end to a mechanical device or fixed point outside the permit space.

To facilitate non-entry rescue, retrieval systems must be used whenever an authorized entrant enters a permit space, unless the retrieval equipment would increase the overall risk of entry.

A mechanical device must be available to retrieve personnel from vertical-type permit spaces that are more than 5 feet deep.

Module Fifteen

Control of Hazardous Energy (Lockout/Tagout), Part 1

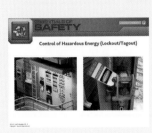

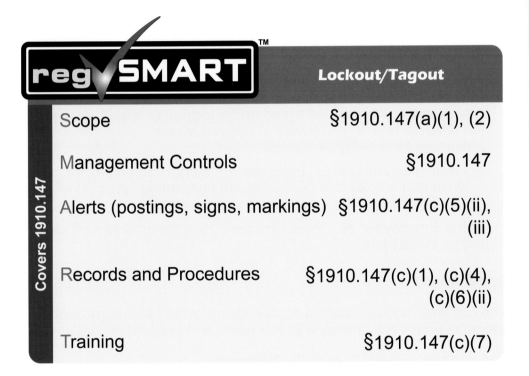

Covers 1910.147

regSMART	Lockout/Tagout
Scope	§1910.147(a)(1), (2)
Management Controls	§1910.147
Alerts (postings, signs, markings)	§1910.147(c)(5)(ii), (iii)
Records and Procedures	§1910.147(c)(1), (c)(4), (c)(6)(ii)
Training	§1910.147(c)(7)

Lockout/Tagout General Requirements

Definitions:

> **Lockout/Tagout**: The act of isolating energy sources, as well as any residual energy, during servicing and maintenance of machines or equipment in accordance with an established procedure

> **Energy Source**: Any source of electrical, mechanical, hydraulic, pneumatic, chemical, thermal, or other energy

> **Authorized Employee**: A person who locks out or tags out machines or equipment in order to perform servicing or maintenance on that machine or equipment

> **Affected Employee**: An employee whose job requires him or her to operate or use a machine or equipment on which servicing or maintenance is being performed under lockout or tagout, or whose job requires him or her to work in an area in which such servicing or maintenance is being performed

>> An "affected employee" becomes an "authorized employee" when that employee's duties include performing servicing or maintenance on the equipment in question.

> **Other Employee**: All others who may be in the area when lockout/tagout takes place

Application:

The Lockout/Tagout Standard applies to the control of energy during servicing and/or maintenance of machines and equipment.

The Standard does not cover the following:

> certain normal production operations

>> Minor tool changes, adjustments, and other minor servicing activities that take place during normal production operations are not covered by the Standard if they are routine, repetitive, and integral to the use of the equipment for production, provided that the work is performed using alternative measures, such as machine guarding, that provide effective protection.

» Servicing and/or maintenance that takes place during normal production operations is covered by the Standard only if an employee is required to remove or bypass a guard or other safety device, or an employee is required to place any part of his or her body into the point of operation or where an associated danger zone exists during a machine operating cycle.

⟩ work on cord- and plug-connected electric equipment if the unexpected start-up or energization of the equipment is controlled by unplugging the equipment from the electrical source, and the plug is under the exclusive control of the employee performing the servicing or maintenance

⟩ certain hot tap operations

» **Hot Tap Operation**: A procedure used in repair, maintenance, and service activities that involves welding on a piece of equipment under pressure in order to connect something

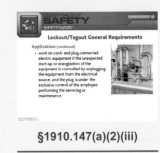

§1910.147(a)(2)(iii)

§1910.147(a)(2)

⟩ electric utilization installations that are covered by Subpart S, Electrical, of the OSHA regulations, and installations under the exclusive control of electric utilities for the purpose of power generation, transmission, and distribution

» **Utilization Equipment**: Equipment that utilizes electric energy for electronic, electromechanical, chemical, heating, lighting, or similar purposes

⟩ oil and gas well drilling and servicing

⟩ construction, agriculture, or shipyard/marine terminal/longshoring employment

Electrical Lockout/Tagout

Electrical lockout/tagout is discussed in §1910.333(b).

Note: Lockout/tagout procedures that comply with the Lockout/Tagout Standard's requirements will be deemed to comply with the electrical lockout/tagout requirements of §1910.333(b), so long as: (1) the procedures address the electrical safety hazards covered by Subpart S; (2) a tag used without a lock is supplemented by at least one additional safety measure that equivalent safety as that obtained by use of a lock; and (3) a qualified person uses test equipment to test the circuit elements and electrical parts to verify that they are deenergized and that there is no inadvertently induced voltage or unrelated voltage backfeed.

General Rules:

While any employee is exposed to contact with parts of fixed electric equipment or circuits that have been de-energized, the circuits energizing the parts shall be locked out, tagged out, or both.

The employer shall maintain a written copy of the required lockout/tagout procedures.

Electrical Procedures:

The following requirements must be followed in the order presented:

> Safe procedures for de-energizing circuits and equipment shall be determined before circuits or equipment are de-energized.

> The circuits and equipment to be worked on shall be disconnected from all electric energy sources.

>> Control circuit devices (push buttons, selector switch, interlocks, etc.) may not be used as the sole means for de-energizing circuits or equipment.

>> Interlocks for electrical equipment may not be used as a substitute for lockout/tagout procedures.

§1910.333(b)(2), Note 1

§1910.333(b)(2)(i)

§1910.333(b)(2)(i), (ii)

⟩ Stored electrical energy that might endanger personnel shall be released.

　》 Capacitors shall be discharged.

　》 High-capacitance elements shall be short-circuited and grounded.

　》 If the capacitors or associated equipment are handled, they must be treated as energized.

⟩ Stored non-electrical energy in devices that could re-energize electric circuit parts shall be blocked or relieved to the extent that the circuit parts could not be accidentally energized.

⟩ A lock and a tag shall be placed on each disconnected means. **See the "Locks and Tags" subsection for more information.**

⟩ A qualified person must verify the de-energized condition.

　》 The qualified person must operate the controls or otherwise verify that the equipment cannot be restarted.

　》 The qualified person must use test equipment to test the circuit elements and electrical parts and verify that all elements and parts are de-energized.

⟩ Before circuits or equipment are re-energized, even temporarily, these requirements must be met in the order given:

　1. A qualified person shall conduct tests and visual inspections, as necessary, to verify that all tools, electrical jumpers, shorts, grounds, etc. have been removed so that the circuits and equipment can be safety energized.

　2. Employees exposed to the hazards associated with re-energizing the circuit or equipment shall be warned to stay clear of circuits and equipment.

　3. Each lock and tag shall be removed by the employee who applied it or under his/her direct supervision. See the "Locks and Tags" subsection for more information.

　4. There shall be a visual determination that all employees are clear of the circuits and equipment.

§1910.333(b)(2)(ii)[A]–[C]

§1910.333(b)(2)(ii)[D], (iii)[A]

§1910.333(b)(2)(v)

§1910.333(b)

§1910.333(b)(2)(iii)

§1910.147(c)(1)

§1910.147(c)(4)(ii)

Locks and Tags:

A lock and a tag shall be placed on each disconnected means used to de-energize circuits and equipment on which work is to be performed.

The lock shall be attached so as to prevent persons from operating the disconnecting means unless they resort to undue force or the use of tools.

Each tag shall contain a statement prohibiting unauthorized operation of the disconnecting means and removal of the tag.

If a lock cannot be applied, or if the employer can demonstrate that tagging procedures will provide a level of safety equivalent to that obtained by the use of a lock, a tag may be used without a lock. However, this may be done only if:

›   only one circuit or piece of equipment is de-energized;

›   the lockout period does not extend beyond the work shift;

›   employees exposed to the hazards associated with re-energizing the circuit are familiar with this procedure; and

›   at least one additional safety measure that provides a level of safety equivalent to that obtained by the use of a lock (e.g., removal of an isolating circuit element, blocking of a controlling switch, or opening of an extra disconnecting device) is used.

Lockout/Tagout Energy Control Program

The employer must establish a program to ensure that before any employee performs any servicing or maintenance on machines or equipment where the unexpected energizing, start-up, or release of stored energy could occur and cause injury, the machines or equipment are isolated from the energy source and rendered inoperative. The program shall consist of:

›   energy control procedures;

›   employee training; and

›   periodic inspections.

The lockout/tagout procedures shall clearly and specifically outline:

›   scope and purpose

›   who has authorization for lockout/tagout

> the rules and techniques used for lockout/tagout
> the means to enforce lockout/tagout procedures
> specific statement of the intended use of the procedure
> specific procedural steps for:
>> shutting down, isolating, blocking, and securing machines or equipment,
>> placement, removal, and the transfer of lockout/tagout devices, and responsibility for them, and
>> specific requirements for testing a machine or equipment to determine and verify the effectiveness of lockout/tagout devices

§1910.147(c)(4)(ii)

TNT
Test and Try or you may DIE!!

§1910.147(c)(5)(i)

Lockout/Tagout Devices

Types of lockout/tagout devices:

> locks	> key blocks
> tags	> adapter pins
> chains	> self-locking fasteners
> wedges	> other hardware to isolate, secure, or block machines or equipment from energy sources

§1910.147(c)(5)(ii)[B]

Lockout and tagout devices shall be standardized within the facility in at least one of the following:

Color	Size	Shape

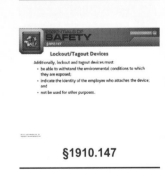

§1910.147

Additionally, lockout and tagout devices must:

> be able to withstand the environmental conditions to which they are exposed;
> indicate the identity of the employee who attaches the device; and
> not be used for other purposes.

§1910.147(c)(5)(ii)[C][2]

§1910.147(c)(5)(iii)

§1910.147(c)(6)(i)[A], [B]

Tagout devices must meet these additional requirements:

> Tags must be standardized in print and format.

> Tags must be constructed and printed so that exposure to weather conditions or wet/damp locations will not cause the tag to deteriorate or the message on the tag to become illegible.

> Tags, including the means of attachment, must be substantial enough to prevent inadvertent or accidental removal.

>> Tagout device attachment means shall be of a non-reusable type, attachable by hand, self-locking, and non-releasable with a minimum unlocking strength of no less than 50 pounds, meaning it is equivalent to a one-piece, all-environment-tolerant nylon cable tie.

> Tagout devices must warn against the hazardous conditions that will be created if the machine or equipment is energized. Following are some legend examples:

>> Do Not Start.

>> Do Not Open.

>> Do Not Close.

>> Do Not Energize.

>> Do Not Operate.

Periodic Inspections of Lockout/Tagout Procedures

Employers must conduct a periodic inspection of the energy control procedure at least annually.

> This is to ensure that the procedure and the requirements of this Standard are being followed.

> The company-authorized inspector of the procedure cannot be the person using the procedure being inspected.

> The period inspection shall be conducted to correct any deviations or inadequacies identified.

> If lockout is used for energy control, the periodic inspection must include a review between the inspector and each authorized employee of that employee's responsibilities under the energy control procedure being inspected.

> Where lockout or tagout is used for energy control procedures, the periodic inspection must include a review between the inspector and each authorized and affected employee of that employee's responsibilities under the energy control procedure being inspected and the tagout training elements discussed in the next section.

The employer shall certify the periodic inspections have been performed. The certification shall identify the:

> machine or equipment on which the energy control procedure was being utilized;

> date of the inspection;

> employees included in the inspection; and

> person performing the inspection.

§1910.147(c)(6)(i)[C], [D]

§1910.147(c)(6)(ii)

TM

OSHA Letter of Interpretation — 03/09/2004: Civic

Equipment with similar types of hazardous energy and that have similar types of controls can be grouped and inspected by the type of procedure.

A grouping of detailed individual procedures would be considered a single procedure for periodic inspection purposes if all of the procedures in the grouping have similar:

> intended equipment use;

> procedural steps for shutting down, isolating, blocking, and securing equipment;

> procedural steps for the placement, removal, and transfer of the lockout or tagout devices and the responsibility for them; and

> requirements for testing equipment to determine and verify the effectiveness of lockout/tagout devices and other control measures.

§1910.147(c)(7)(i)[A], [B]

§1910.147(c)(7)(i)[A, B]

§1910.147(c)(7)(i)[C]

§1910.147(c)(7)

Training

The employer shall provide training to ensure that:

> the purpose and function of the energy control program are understood by employees; and

> the knowledge and skills required for the safe application, usage, and removal of the energy controls are acquired by employees.

The training must include the following:

> **Authorized employees** must receive training in:

>> the recognition of applicable hazardous energy sources,

>> the type and magnitude of the energy available in the workplace, and

>> the methods and means necessary for energy isolation and control.

> **Affected employees** must be instructed in the purpose and use of the energy control procedure.

> **Other employees** whose work operations are or may be in an area where energy control procedures may be utilized must be instructed:

>> about the procedure, and

>> on the prohibition against attempts to restart or re-energize machines or equipment that is locked out or tagged out.

> When **tagout systems** are used, employees must also be trained on the following limitations of tags:

>> Tags are essentially warning devices attached to energy isolating devices and do not provide the physical restraint that is provided by a lock.

>> When a tag is attached to an energy isolating means, it is not to be removed without authorization of the authorized person responsible for it; it is never to be bypassed, ignored, or otherwise defeated.

>> In order to be effective, tags must be legible and understandable by all authorized employees, affected employees, and all other employees whose work operations are or may be in the area.

» Tags and their means of attachment must be made of materials that will withstand the environmental conditions encountered in the workplace.

» Tags may evoke a false sense of security; their meaning needs to be understood as part of the overall energy control program.

» Tags must be securely attached to energy isolating devices so that they cannot be inadvertently or accidentally detached during use.

§1910.147(c)(7)

Retraining shall be provided for all authorized and affected employees whenever there is a change in:

› job assignments;

› machines;

› equipment or processes that present a new hazard; or

› energy control procedures.

§1910.147(c)(7)(iii)[A]

Additional retraining must be conducted whenever a periodic inspection reveals, or the employer has reason to believe, that there are deviations from procedures or there are inadequacies in the employee's knowledge or use of the energy control procedures.

The employer shall certify that employee training has been accomplished and is being kept up to date. The certification must contain each employee's name and dates of training.

§1910.147(c)(7)(iii)[B], (iv)

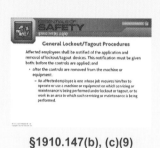

General Lockout/Tagout Procedures

Lockout or tagout shall be performed only by the authorized employees who are performing the servicing or maintenance.

> An authorized person is the one who locks out or tags out machines or equipment in order to perform servicing or maintenance on that machine or equipment.

Affected employees shall be notified of the application and removal of lockout/tagout devices. This notification must be given both: before the controls are applied; and

> after the controls are removed from the machine or equipment.

>> An affected employee is one whose job requires him/her to operate or use a machine or equipment on which servicing or maintenance is being performed under lockout or tagout, or to work in an area in which such servicing or maintenance is being performed.

Elements of the Lockout/Tagout Procedure

The following sequence must be used for the energy control procedure:

1) Preparation for Shutdown

Before an authorized or affected employee turns off a machine or equipment, the authorized employee must have knowledge of:

> type and magnitude of the energy;

> hazards of the energy to be controlled; and

> method or means to control the energy.

2) Machine or Equipment Shutdown

The machine or equipment shall be turned off or shut down using the established procedures.

> An orderly shutdown must be utilized to avoid any additional or increased hazards to employees as a result of the equipment stoppage.

3) Machine or Equipment Isolation

All energy isolating devices that are needed to control the energy must be physically located and operated in such a manner as to isolate the machine or equipment from all energy sources.

4) Lockout or Tagout Device Application

Lockout or tagout devices shall be affixed to each energy isolating device by authorized employees.

> Lockout devices must be affixed in a manner that will hold the energy isolating devices in a "safe" or "off" position.

> Tagout devices must be affixed in such a manner as will clearly indicate that the operation or movement of energy isolating devices is prohibited.

5) Stored Energy

All potentially hazardous stored or residual energy shall be:

> relieved;

> disconnected;

> restrained; and

> otherwise rendered safe.

If there is a possibility of re-accumulation of stored energy to a hazardous level, verification of isolation shall be continued until the servicing or maintenance is completed or until the possibility of such accumulation no longer exists.

6) Verification of Isolation

Prior to starting work on machines or equipment that has been locked out or tagged out, the authorized employee must verify that isolation and de-energization of the machine or equipment has been accomplished.

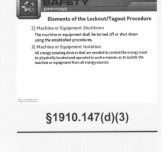

§1910.147(d)(3)

§1910.147(d)(4)

§1910.147(d)(5)

§1910.147(d)(6)

§1910.147(e)

7) Release from Lockout or Tagout

Before lockout/tagout devices are removed and energy is restored to the machine or equipment, the authorized employee must:

› inspect the work area to ensure that nonessential items have been removed and that machine or equipment components are operationally intact;

› check to ensure that all employees have been safely positioned or removed;

› notify all affected employees that the lockout/tagout devices have been removed (**Note**: This is done after the devices are removed, but before start-up.); and

› ensure that each lockout/tagout device is removed from each energy isolating device by the employee who applied it.

Special Requirements for Lockout/Tagout

When the authorized employee who applied the lockout/tagout device is not available to remove it, that device may be removed under the direction of the employer so long as specific procedures and training for such removal have been developed, documented, and incorporated into the energy control program.

The specific procedure must:

› provide equivalent safety to the removal of the device by the authorized employee who applied it; and

› include at least the following elements:

» verification by the employer that the authorized employee who applied the device is not at the facility,

» making all reasonable efforts to contact the authorized employee to inform him/her that the lockout/tagout device has been removed, and

» ensuring that the authorized employee has this knowledge before he/she resumes work at the facility.

Temporary Removal of Devices

In situations in which lockout/tagout devices must be temporarily removed and the machine or equipment energized to test or position the equipment, the following sequence of actions shall be followed:

1. Clear the machine or equipment of tools and materials.

2. Remove employees from the machine or equipment area.

3. Remove the lockout or tagout devices.

4. Energize and proceed with testing or positioning.

5. De-energize all systems and reapply energy control measures to continue servicing the equipment.

Outside Personnel (Contractors)

Whenever outside servicing personnel are to be engaged in maintenance activities:

> The onsite employer and the outside employer shall inform each other of their respective lockout or tagout procedures.

> The onsite employer shall ensure that employees understand and comply with the restrictions and prohibitions of the outside employer's energy control program.

§1910.147(f)(1)

§1910.147(f)(2)

§1910.147(f)(3)

§1910.147(f)(4)

Group Lockout or Tagout

Primary responsibility is vested in an authorized employee for a set number of employees working under the protection of a group lockout or tagout device. That authorized employee must determine the exposure status of individual group members with regard to the lockout or tagout of the equipment.

When more than one crew, craft, or department is involved, an authorized employee must be assigned the following overall job-associated lockout/tagout control responsibilities:

› coordination of affected work forces

› ensuring the continuity of protection

Each authorized employee shall:

› affix a personal lockout or tagout device to the group lockout device when he or she begins work; and

› remove those devices when he or she stops working on the equipment being serviced.

OSHA Letter of Interpretation — 11/03/99: De Vito

Work authorization permits may play a role in an employer's group lockout/tagout procedures. A work authorization permit is a document authorizing employees to perform specific tasks. While the Lockout/Tagout Standard does not specifically require the use of a work authorization permit, these documents may be used as a means of achieving compliance with the group lockout or tagout requirements

Shift or Personnel Changes

Specific procedures shall be utilized during shift or personnel changes to ensure the continuity of lockout or tagout protection.

› These are procedures for the orderly transfer of lockout or tagout device protection between off-going and on-coming employees.

› This is to minimize exposure to hazards from the unexpected energization or start-up of the equipment or the release of stored energy.

Module Sixteen

Materials Handling and Storage

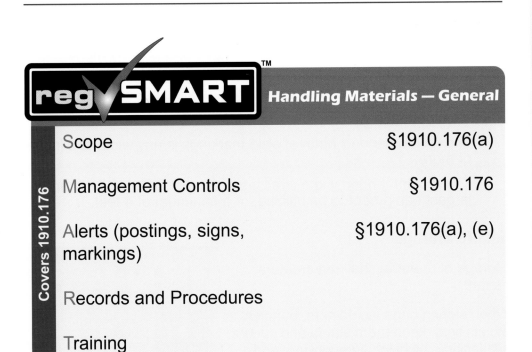

reg✓SMART™ **Handling Materials — General**

Covers 1910.176

Scope	§1910.176(a)
Management Controls	§1910.176
Alerts (postings, signs, markings)	§1910.176(a), (e)
Records and Procedures	
Training	

regSMART

§1910.176(a)

§1910.176(b)

§1910.176(c)

Materials Handling and Storage

Clearances

Where mechanical handling equipment is used, sufficient safe clearances shall be allowed for aisles, at loading docks, through doorways, and wherever turns or passage must be made.

Aisles and passageways shall be kept clear and in good repair, with no obstruction across or in aisles that could create a hazard.

Permanent aisles and passageways shall be appropriately marked.

> The lines used to delineate the aisles may be any color so long as they clearly define the area considered as aisle space.

> Recommendations:

>> The recommended width of aisle markings is any width of 2 inches or more.

>> The recommended width of aisles is at least 3 feet wider than the largest equipment to be utilized, or a minimum of 4 feet.

Secure Storage

Storage of material shall not create a hazard.

When storing bags, containers, bundles, etc., in tiers, keep them stable and secure by stacking, blocking, interlocking, and limiting them in height to prevent tiers from sliding or collapsing.

Housekeeping

Storage areas shall be kept free from accumulation of materials that constitute hazards from:

> tripping;

> fire;

> explosion; or

> pest harborage

Vegetation must be controlled when necessary.

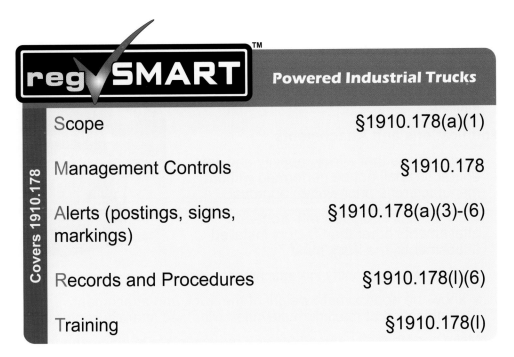

regSMART™	Powered Industrial Trucks
Scope	§1910.178(a)(1)
Management Controls	§1910.178
Alerts (postings, signs, markings)	§1910.178(a)(3)-(6)
Records and Procedures	§1910.178(l)(6)
Training	§1910.178(l)

Covers 1910.178

Powered Industrial Trucks

This section contains safety requirements relating to fire protection, design, maintenance, and use of:

› fork trucks

› tractors

› platform lift trucks

› motorized hand trucks

› other specialized industrial trucks powered by:

» electric motors, or

» internal combustion engines

Forklifts, also known as powered industrial trucks, are used in numerous work settings, primarily to move materials.

Classroom Discussion: Different Forklifts = Different Hazards

Handout: Different Forklifts = Different Hazards

› Have any of you worked with any of these types of forklifts?

› Why do these forklifts pose the types of hazards listed?

› What are some things you can do to ensure that these types of accidents do not occur?

regSMART

§1910.178(a)

Discussion

Forklift-Related Incidents

› Each year in the United States, nearly 100 workers are killed and another 20,000 are injured.

Modifications and Attachments

› Modifications that affect capacity and safe operation shall not be performed without manufacturer's prior written approval.

› If the truck is equipped with front-end attachments other than factory installed attachments, the truck must:

» be marked to identify the attachments, and

» show the approximate weight of the truck and attachment combination at maximum elevation with load laterally centered.

› Make sure that all nameplates and markings are in place and are maintained in a legible condition.

Safety Guards

› High lift rider trucks shall be fitted with an overhead guard.

Fueling and Recharging Operations

Fuel Handling and Storage

› The storage and handling of liquefied petroleum gas fuel shall be in accordance with NFPA Storage and Handling of Liquefied Petroleum Gases (NFPA No. 58-1969).

› The storage and handling of gasoline and diesel fuel shall be in accordance with NFPA Flammable and Combustible Liquids Code (NFPA No. 30-1969).

Changing and Charging Storage Batteries

› Locate battery charging installation in areas designated for that purpose.

› Provide facilities for flushing and neutralizing spilled electrolyte.

› Provide fire protection.

› Protect charging apparatus from damage by trucks.

› Provide adequate ventilation for dispersal of vapors from gassing batteries.

> Use a conveyor, overhead hoist, or equivalent material-handling equipment to handle batteries.

> Use a carboy tilter or siphon to handle electrolyte.

> Open the battery or compartment cover(s) to dissipate heat.

> Prohibit smoking in the charging area.

> Take precautions to prevent open flames, sparks, and electric arcs in battery charging areas.

> Do not pour water into acid—always pour acid into water.

> Keep tools and other metallic object away from the tops of uncovered batteries.

> Ensure eyewash facilities are readily available in the designated battery charging area.

Eye/Face Wash and Shower Units

> ANSI Z358.1 establishes minimum performance and use requirements for eyewash and showers.

» Pressure

> Pressure should be at a velocity low enough to be non-injurious to the user.

» Temperature

> Flushing fluid temperature must be tepid—between 80-95°F is recommended.

» Time/amount

> Eye/face wash units must deliver a minimum of 3.0 gal/min for 15 min.

> Eye wash only units must deliver 0.4 gal/min for 15 min.

> Showers must deliver a minimum of 20 gal/min for 15 min.

» All plumbed units

> All plumbed units must be operated and tested weekly for accurate maintenance.

» Portable units

> Additives may be required for water stability.

§1910.178(g)

ANSI Z358.1

§1910.178(k)(1)

Directive STD 01-11-007

§1910.178(k)(3)

§1910.178(l)

Trucks and Railroad Cars

The brakes of highway trucks shall be set and wheel chocks placed under the rear wheels to prevent the trucks from rolling while they are boarded with powered industrial trucks.

Directive STD 01-11-007 allows for a mechanical device to secure the truck or trailer to the dock instead of chocking the wheels.

> The mechanical device attaches to a bar on the back of the truck or trailer commonly referred to as the "ICC bar."

This is a broken ICC bar on a truck
The dock lock would not be effective on this truck,
so wheel chocks would be needed.

Fixed jacks may be necessary to support a semi trailer and prevent up-ending during the loading or unloading when the trailer is not coupled to a tractor.

Operator Training

Training shall consist of a combination of:

> formal instruction;

> practical training; and

> evaluation of the operator's performance.

All operator training and evaluation shall be conducted by persons who have:

> knowledge;

> training; and

> experience.

Training program content shall include:

> truck-related topics;

> workplace-related topics; and

> regulation topics.

Refresher Training and Evaluation:

> Refresher training or an evaluation of previous training is required at least every 3 years.

> Remedial training is required for cases of:

>> any forklift accident, near-miss accident, or instance of unsafe operation,

>> any evaluation indicating that the operator needs retraining, or

>> any assignment for which the operator must drive another type of forklift or work in substantially different or changed conditions.

> The trainer who does the refresher training must perform an evaluation to ensure its effectiveness.

Certification:

> Certify that each operator has been trained and evaluated.

> Include the following in the certification:

>> name of the operator

>> date of the training

>> date of the evaluation

>> identity of the persons performing the training and/or evaluation

Forklift Stability

"Moment"

Tipping over is probably the most dangerous hazard faced by forklift operators, especially with any kind of high-lift truck. Forklifts can tip over from front to back or from side to side if the "moment" of a load is greater than that of the vehicle. Basically, the "moment" of something is the product of its weight multiplied by its distance from a fixed point. The greater the weight of something or the greater its distance from a fixed point, the greater its moment.

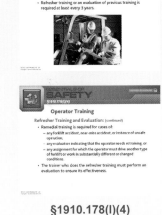

§1910.178(l)

§1910.178(l)(4)

§1910.178(l)(6)

§1910.178 Appendix A

Stability Triangle

The stability triangle is an area based on the 3-point suspension system found in most forklifts. The center of gravity is the point at which all of an object's weight is concentrated. As long as a load's center of gravity is located within the stability triangle, the vehicle will not tip over. If the load is too heavy, is too high, or is moved too quickly, the center of gravity can shift outside of the stability triangle. This will cause the vehicle to become unstable and to possibly tip over.

Load Capacity

Load charts, identification plates, and load capacity plates will assist in determining how large of a load a forklift is able to carry. Never exceed the manufacturer's rated load capacity.

Also, never rely on the common name of a forklift when determining its load capacity. For example, one of the most common warehouse-style forklifts is frequently called a "5,000-pound forklift." It is typically equipped with a 3-stage straight mast, and usually, has about a 15-foot lifting height with a side-shift feature. However, this "5,000-pound forklift" is rated to carry only 3,700 pounds according to its identification plate!

Operating Forklifts Safely

Truck Operations

> Trucks shall not be driven up to anyone standing in front of a bench or other fixed object.

> No person shall be allowed to stand or pass under the elevated portion of any truck, whether loaded or empty.

> Only approved industrial trucks shall be used in hazardous locations.

> Unauthorized personnel shall not be permitted to ride on powered industrial trucks. A safe place to ride must be provided when riding of trucks is authorized.

> When a powered industrial truck is left unattended, the load-engaging means shall be fully lowered, controls shall be neutralized, power shall be shut off, and the brakes set. Wheels shall be blocked if the truck is parked on an incline.

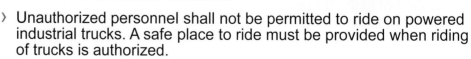

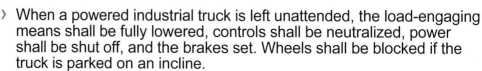

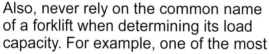

> Ensure that forklifts have sufficient headroom above them for all operations.

> Unless operating conditions do no permit doing so, an overhead guard must be used to protect the operator from falling objects.

> When the type of load presents a hazard to the operator, the forklift must have a vertical load backrest extension.

> Do not use forklifts to open or close freight doors.

Note: Employees must use seat belts and other operator restraint systems if they have been provided by the manufacturer for the particular forklift.

Note: Forklift operators must be at least 18 years of age under federal labor regulations.

Traveling with Trucks

> All traffic regulations shall be observed, including authorized speed limits (set by employer).

> Where vision is obstructed, the driver shall be required to:

>> slow down, and

>> sound the horn at cross aisles.

> Stunt driving and horseplay shall not be permitted.

> Arms and legs must not be placed between the uprights of the mast or outside the running lines of the truck.

> Operators must maintain a safe distance from the edges of ramps and platforms.

Powered Industrial Truck Maintenance

Open flames shall not be used for checking:

> electrolyte level in storage batteries; or

> gasoline level in fuel tanks

Inspect forklifts:

> before being used;

> at least daily; and

> after each shift when industrial trucks are used on a round-the-clock basis.

Refer to the "Forklift Operator's Daily Checklist" in your Student Workbook.

§1910.178(m)

Section 5(a) of the OSH Act; OSHA Letter of Interpretation

§1910.178(n)(1), (4)

§1910.178(m)(4), (m)(6), (n)(9)

§1910.178(p)(5), (q)(7)

Case Study 1

Case Study 2

Case Study 3

Case Study 1

The Incident

A person was riding on the forks of a forklift as it approached an intersection; the forklift operator slowed down and turned his head to check for oncoming traffic.

When he turned his head back, he could not see the person that was on the forks. He stopped the forklift and found out he had run over the worker who was lying underneath the right side of the forklift.

Incident Prevention

What could prevent this incident from happening?

Case Study 2

The Incident

A wooden pallet was placed on top of the forks of a forklift, and a worker then stood on the pallet. The forklift operator raised the forks 16 feet above the concrete floor to the top of the storage rack.

While the worker was placing a few tires on the pallet, the forklift operator noticed that the pallet was becoming unstable, but it was too late. The worker lost his balance and fell, striking his head on the floor.

Incident Prevention

What could prevent this incident from happening?

Case Study 3

The Incident

A forklift was traveling in reverse at high speed down an aisle when the forklift hit a metal scrap bin, pushing it toward a punch press. Multiple impacts between the scrap bin, forklift, and press ultimately crushed the press operator.

Incident Prevention

What could prevent this incident from happening?

Module Seventeen

Machine Guarding

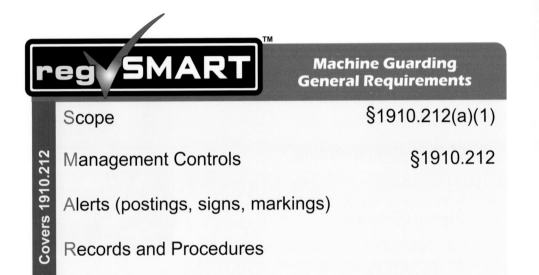

reg✓SMART™ **Machine Guarding General Requirements**

Covers 1910.212

Scope	§1910.212(a)(1)
Management Controls	§1910.212
Alerts (postings, signs, markings)	
Records and Procedures	
Training	

Machine Guarding

Scope §1910.212(a)(1)
Management Controls §1910.212
Alerts
Records and Procedures
Training

regSMART

§1910.212(a)(1)

§1910.212(a)(2)

§1910.212(a)(3)(i), (ii)

§1910.212(a)(3)(iii)

General Requirements for All Machines

One or more methods of machine guarding must be provided to protect the operator and other employees in the machine area from hazards such as those created by:

> point of operation
> in-going nip points
> rotating parts
> flying chips
> sparks

Guards shall be affixed to the machine where possible and secured elsewhere if for any reason attachment to the machine is not possible.

Note: There are no grandfather clauses for machine guarding.

Point-of-Operation Guarding

The point of operation is the area on a machine where work is actually performed upon the material being processed.

The point of operation of machines whose operation exposes an employee to injury shall be guarded to prevent the operator from having any body part in the danger zone during the operating cycle.

Special Hand Tools

Special hand tools for placing and removing material shall permit easy handling of material without the operator placing a hand in the danger zone.

> Special tools shall not be used in lieu of other guarding, but can only be used to supplement protection provided.

The following are some of the machines that usually require point of operation guarding:

> guillotine cutters   > power saws

> shears   > portable power tools

> power presses   > forming rolls

> milling machines   > calendars

Methods of machine safeguarding include the following:

> presence sensing:

>> photoelectrical (optical)

>> radio frequency (capacitance)

>> pressure-sensitive mats

> electromechanical:

>> interlocked guards

>> safety controls

>> safety trip control

>> two-hand control

> mechanical:

>> fixed guards

>> adjustable and self-adjusting guards

>> pullbacks and restraining devices (**Note:** not used very often today)

§1910.212(a)(3)(iv)

"Concepts and Techniques of Machine Safeguarding"

Exposure of Fan Blades

When the blades of a fan are less than 7 feet above the floor, the blades shall be guarded.

> The guard shall have openings no larger than ½ inch.

Anchoring Fixed Machinery

Machines designed for a fixed location shall be securely anchored to prevent walking or moving.

reg✓SMART™

Abrasive Wheel Machinery

Covers 1910.215

Scope	§1910.215(a)(1), (a)(5)
Management Controls	§1910.215
Alerts (postings, signs, markings)	§1910.215(d)(1)
Records and Procedures	
Training	

Abrasive Wheel Machinery

Work Rests

Work rests shall be kept adjusted closely to the wheel with a maximum opening of 1/8 inch to prevent the work from being jammed between the wheel and the rest, which may cause wheel breakage.

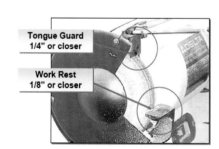

Tongue Guard
1/4" or closer

Work Rest
1/8" or closer

Tongue Guard Adjustment

The distance between the wheel and the adjustable tongue guard shall never exceed ¼ inch.

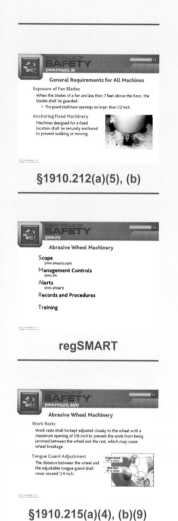

§1910.212(a)(5), (b)

regSMART

§1910.215(a)(4), (b)(9)

Inspections

Immediately before mounting:

> Check the spindle speed of the machine.

>> The spindle speed must not exceed the maximum operating speed marked on the wheel.

> Perform a ring test:

>> Tap the wheel gently with a light, non-metallic implement, such as the handle of a screwdriver, at approximately 45° on each side of the wheel, 1 or 2 inches from the outer edge.

>> Then, rotate the wheel 45° and repeat the test.

>> An undamaged wheel will give a clear, metallic tone. If the wheel is cracked, there will be a dead sound and not a clear "ring."

>> If the wheel sounds cracked, do not use it.

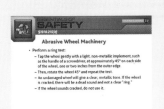

§1910.215(d)

regSMART

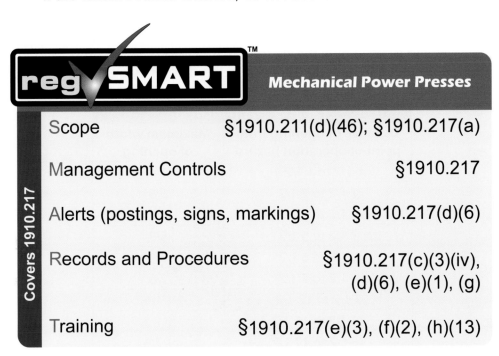

reg✓SMART™ **Mechanical Power Presses**

Covers 1910.217

Scope	§1910.211(d)(46); §1910.217(a)
Management Controls	§1910.217
Alerts (postings, signs, markings)	§1910.217(d)(6)
Records and Procedures	§1910.217(c)(3)(iv), (d)(6), (e)(1), (g)
Training	§1910.217(e)(3), (f)(2), (h)(13)

Mechanical Power Presses

§1910.217(c)(1), (4)

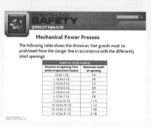

§1910.217 Table O-10

Safety STOP ™

OSHA Note — §1910.211(d)(45)

Point of operation is the area of the press where material is actually positioned and work is being performed during any process such as shearing, punching, forming, or assembling.

Safeguarding the Point of Operation

It is the responsibility of the employer to provide and ensure the use of point-of-operation guards or properly applied and adjusted point-of-operation devices on every operation performed on a mechanical power press.

> This does not apply when the point of operation opening is ¼ inch or less.

> Hand feeding tools are not point-of-operation or protection devices and may not be used instead of the required guards.

The following table shows the distances that guards must be positioned from the danger line in accordance with the differently sized openings:

Table O-10 [in inches]	
Distance of opening from point-of-operation hazard	**Maximum width of opening**
1/2 to 1 1/2	1/4
1 1/2 to 2 1/2	3/8
2 1/2 to 3 1/2	1/2
3 1/2 to 5 1/2	5/8
5 1/2 to 6 1/2	3/4
6 1/2 to 7 1/2	7/8
7 1/2 to 12 1/2	1 1/4
12 1/2 to 15 1/2	1 1/2
15 1/2 to 17 1/2	1 7/8
17 1/2 to 31 1/2	2 1/8

Inspection, Maintenance, and Modification of Presses

Employers must establish and follow a program of periodic and regular inspections of power presses to ensure that all their parts, auxiliary equipment, and safeguards are in a safe operating condition and adjustment.

Each press must be inspected at least weekly to determine the condition of the clutch/brake mechanism, antirepeat feature, and single stroke mechanism.

The employer shall maintain a certification record of inspections, tests, and maintenance work that includes:

> date of the inspection, test, or maintenance

> signature of the person who performed the inspection, test, or maintenance

> serial number or other identifier of the press that was inspected, tested, or maintained.

It shall be the responsibility of any person modifying a power press to furnish instructions with the modification to establish new or changed guidelines for the use and care of the power press so modified.

Operating Rules

Some of the more important rules for power presses include (not a complete list):

> **PSDI Mode**: Presence-sensing devices may not be used to start a slide motion except when used in total conformance with §1910.217(h), which is quite detailed and requires certification of the control system. Presence-sensing devices may not be used on machines with full revolution clutches.

> **Hand/Foot Operations**: Hand/foot operations must have guards to prevent accidental start-up.

> **Full-Revolution Clutches**: All machines using full-revolution positive clutches must have a single-stroke mechanism.

> **Main Disconnect Switch**: Every control system must have a main disconnect switch capable of being locked in the OFF position.

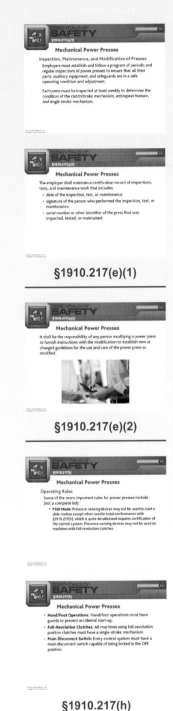

§1910.217(e)(1)

§1910.217(e)(2)

§1910.217(h)

§1910.217(g);
OSHA Form 1218-0070

§1910.217(c)(3)(iii)[e]

Injury Reports

The employer shall, within 30 days of the occurrence, report to OSHA all mechanical power press point-of-operation injuries to operators or other employees.

The report must include:

> employer's name and the address and location of the workplace;

> employee's name, injury sustained, and the task being performed (operation, set-up, maintenance, or other);

> type of clutch used on the press (full revolution, part revolution, or direct drive);

> type of safeguard(s) being used (two-hand control, two-hand trip, pull-outs, sweeps, or describe any other);

> cause of the accident (repeat or press, safeguard failure, removing stuck part or scrap, no safeguard provided, no safeguard in use, or other);

> type of feeding (manual with hands in dies or with hands out of dies, semi-automatic, automatic, or other);

> means used to actuate press stroke (foot trip, foot control, hand trip, hand control, or other); and

> number of operators required for the operation and the number of operators provided with controls and safeguards.

Safety Distance

The safety distance (D_s) from the sensing field to the point of operation must be greater than the distance determined by the following formula:

D_s = (63 inches/second) x T_s

where:

D_s = minimum safety distance in inches

63 inches/second = Hand speed constant in inches per second

T_s = Stopping time of the press in seconds, measured at approximately 90° position of crankshaft rotation

Training Requirements

Employers must train and instruct the operator in the safe method of working with the press before starting press operations. Adequate supervision is also required so that correct operating procedures are being followed.

§1910.217(f)(2)

§1910.219

OSHA Note — §1910.211(d)(46) and §1910.217(a)

› Mechanical power presses include machines that shear, punch, form, or assemble metal or other material by means of cutting, shaping, or combination dies attached to slides.

› A press consists of a stationary bed or anvil and a slide (or slides) having a controlled reciprocating motion toward and away from the bed surface, the slide being guided in a definite path by the frame of the press.

› Excluded machines:

» Press brakes, hydraulic and pneumatic power presses, bulldozers, hot bending and hot metal presses, forging presses and hammers, riveting machines and similar types of fastener applicators.

Mechanical Power-Transmission Apparatus

"Mechanical power-transmission apparatus" includes all components that transmit energy to the part of the machine performing the work, including:

› flywheels
› pulleys
› belts
› connecting rods
› couplings
› cams
› spindles
› chains
› cranks
› gears

Any moving part of mechanical power-transmission apparatus that is 7 feet or less above the floor or platform shall be guarded.

Consensus Standards

Related Standards

OSHA Standard	Consensus Standard	Title
§1910.213	ANSI O1.1	Woodworking machinery requirements
§1910.215	ANSI B7.1	Abrasive wheels machinery
§1910.216	ANSI B28.1	Mills and calenders in the rubber and plastics industries
§1910.217	ANSI B11.1	Mechanical power presses
§1910.218	ANSI B24.1	Forging machines
§1910.219	ANSI B15.1 NFPA 79-1994	Mechanical power-transmission apparatus Industrial machinery

Module Eighteen
Electrical Requirements

Electrical Requirements

Covers 1910.301 – .399

Scope	§1910.302; §1910.331; §1910.332
Management Controls	§1910.303-§1910.308; §1910.331-§1910.335
Alerts (postings, signs, and markings)	§1910.303(b)(1)(i), (b)(2), (e)-(f), (g)(2)(iii), (h)(2)(iii), (h)(5)(iii); §1910.304(b)(3)(ii)[C][6], (e)(1)(i), (e)(2)(ii), (f)(1)(vi), (f)(1)(ix), (g)(6)(vii)[B]; §1910.305(b)(3)(iii), (c)(3)(ii), (g)(2)(i), (h)(1), (h)(2), (j)(4)(ii), (j)(4)(iv), (j)(5)(ii), (j)(6)(ii)[C]; §1910.306(c)(6), (g)(1)(iv), (k)(4)(iv)[A]; §1910.307(c), (g)(5); §1910.308(a)(5), (a)(6), (b)(3), (c)(2); §1910.335(b)
Records and Procedures	§1910.304(b)(3)(ii)[C]; §1910.305(j)(6)(ii)(D)(3); §1910.333(b)(2), (c)(9)
Training	§1910.331; §1910.332

regSMART

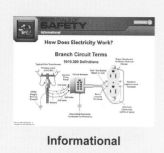

§1910.303(a), (b)

§1910.303(c)(3), (d), (e)

§1910.303(f)

How Does Electricity Work?

Branch Circuit Terms
1910.399 Definitions

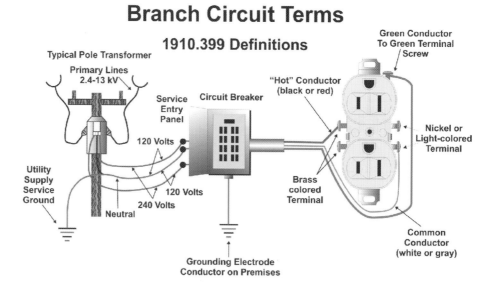

General Requirements

Electrical equipment must meet these general requirements:

> **Approval:** The conductors and equipment shall be acceptable only if approved.

> **Examination:** Electrical equipment shall be free from recognized hazards.

> **Installation and use:** Use or install listed or labeled equipment in accordance with any instructions.

> **Splices:** Conductors shall be spliced or joined with splicing devices suitable for use.

> **Arcing parts:** Electric equipment that produces arcs, sparks, flames, or molten metal shall be enclosed or separated and isolated from all combustible material.

> **Marking:** Electrical equipment must have the manufacturer's name, trademark, and other markings giving voltage, current, wattage, or other ratings as necessary. The markings must be capable of withstanding the environment.

> **Identification of disconnecting means and circuits:** Each disconnecting means, service, feeder, branch circuit, or overcurrent device must be legibly marked to indicate its purpose. Disconnecting means shall be capable of being locked in the open position (which is especially important for lockout/tagout).

› **Working space:** Sufficient access and working space shall be provided and maintained around all electric equipment operating at 600 volts, nominal, or less to ground to permit ready and safe operation and maintenance of such equipment.

§1910.303(g)

Table S-1 — Minimum Depth of Clear Working Space at Electric Equipment, 600 V or Less						
Nominal voltage to ground	**Minimum clear distance for condition[2,3]**					
	Condition A		**Condition B**		**Condition C**	
	m	**ft**	**m**	**ft**	**m**	**ft**
0-150	[1]0.9	[1]3.0	[1]0.9	[1]3.0	0.9	3.0
151-600	[1]0.9	[1]3.0	1.0	3.5	1.2	4.0

Notes to Table S-1:

[1] Minimum clear distances may be 0.7 m (2.5 ft) for installations built before April 16, 1981.

[2] Conditions A, B, and C are as follows:

Condition A – Exposed live parts on one side and no live or grounded parts on the other side of the working space, or exposed live parts on both sides effectively guarded by suitable wood or other insulating material. Insulated wire or insulated busbars operating at not over 300 volts are not considered live parts.

Condition B – Exposed live parts on one side and grounded parts on the other side.

Condition C – Exposed live parts on both sides of the work space (not guarded as provided in Condition A) with the operator between.

[3] Working space is not required in back of assemblies such as dead-front switchboards or motor control centers where there are no renewable or adjustable parts (such as fuses or switches) on the back and where all connections are accessible from locations other than the back. Where rear access is required to work on deenergized parts on the back of enclosed equipment, a minimum working space of 762 mm (30 in.) horizontally shall be provided.

§1910.303 Table S-1

› **Working space (continued):**

» The width of the working space in from of the electrical equipment shall be the width of the equipment or 30 inches, whichever is greater, permitting at least a 90-degree opening of doors or hinged panels.

» The work space must allow at least 6.25 feet of headroom for installations built before August 13, 2007, or 6.5 feet of headroom for installations built on or after August 13, 2007.

» The required workspace may not be used for storage.

§1910.303(g)

Wiring Design and Protection

§1910.304(a)

§1910.304(f)(1)(i), (vi)

§1910.304(f)(1)(iv)

§1910.304(f)(1)(v)

Use and Identification of Grounded and Grounding Conductors

> Conductors used as grounded conductors and equipment-grounding conductors.

> No grounded conductor may be attached so as to reverse designated polarity.

> A grounding terminal or grounding-type device may not be used for purposes other than grounding.

Overcurrent Protection

Conductors and equipment operating at 600 volts, nominal, or less shall be protected from overcurrent in accordance with their ability to safely conduct current. Fuses and circuit breakers shall clearly indicate whether they are in the open (off) or closed (on) position.

Overcurrent devices:

> shall be readily accessible to each employee or building management personnel;

> shall not be located where they could be exposed to physical damage; and

> shall not be located in the vicinity of easily ignitable material.

Fuses and circuit breakers shall be located or shielded so employees will not be burned or injured by their operation.

Note that a fuse is designed to be the weakest link in a circuit. When excess current is drawn through a fuse, the thin strip of conductive metal inside the fuse melts, and the circuit opens. This controlled meltdown will protect the rest of the circuit, including wires, connectors, and equipment. Fuses are not protective devices for people, however, as they will not trip fast enough to protect someone from electrical shock resulting from a short circuit.

Grounding Connections

A grounding electrode conductor shall be used to connect both the equipment grounding conductor and the grounded circuit conductor.

Grounding Path

The path to ground from circuits, equipment, and enclosures shall be permanent and continuous.

§1910.304(g)(4), (5)

Supports, Enclosures, and Equipment to Be Grounded

Supports and enclosures, metal cable trays, metal raceways, and metal enclosures for conductors shall be grounded.

Exposed non-current-carrying metal parts of fixed equipment that may become energized shall be grounded.

Exposed non-current-carrying metal parts of cord- and plug-connected equipment that may become energized shall be grounded.

§1910.304(g)(6)

Wiring Methods, Components, and Equipment

Cabinets, Boxes, and Fittings

Conductors entering boxes, cabinets, or fittings shall also be protected from abrasion. Openings through which conductors enter shall be effectively closed.

Unused openings in cabinets, boxes, and fittings shall be effectively closed.

Covers and Canopies

All pull boxes, junction boxes, and fittings shall be provided with covers approved for the purpose.

If metal covers are used, they shall be grounded.

§1910.305(b)(1)(i), (ii)

§1910.305(b)(2)(i)

§1910.305(b)(3)

§1910.305(c), (d)

Pull and Junction Boxes for Systems Over 600 Volts, Nominal

Boxes shall provide a complete enclosure for the contained conductors or cables.

Boxes shall be closed by suitable covers securely fastened in place.

Covers for boxes shall be permanently marked "HIGH VOLTAGE." The marking shall be on the outside of the box cover and shall be readily visible and legible.

Switches

Single-throw knife switches shall be so connected that the blades are dead when the switch is in the open position.

Switchboards and Panelboards

Switchboards that have any exposed live parts shall be located in permanently dry locations and accessible only to qualified persons.

OSHA Note — §1910.399

› A switchboard is a large single panel, frame, or assembly of panels that has switches, buses, instruments, overcurrent, and other protective devices mounted on the face or back or both. Switchboards are generally accessible from the rear as well as from the front and are not intended to be installed in cabinets.

› A panelboard is a single panel or group of panel units designed for assembly in the form of a single panel, including buses and automatic overcurrent devices, and with or without switches for the control of light, heat, or power circuits. It is designed to be placed in a cabinet or cutout box placed in or against a wall or partition and accessible only from the front.

Enclosures for Damp or Wet Locations

Cabinets, cutout boxes, fittings, boxes, and panelboard enclosures in damp or wet locations shall be weatherproof.

Switches, circuit breakers, and switchboards installed in wet locations shall be enclosed in weatherproof enclosures.

Conductors for General Wiring

All conductors used for general wiring shall be insulated.

GFCI Outlets

A ground fault circuit interrupter (GFCI) is a device intended to protect people by de-energizing a circuit or a portion of a circuit within a set period of time when current to ground exceeds a value less than required to operate the overcurrent protective device of the supply circuit. Follow these rules:

› All 125-volt, single-phase, 15- and 20-amp outlets installed in bathrooms or on rooftops shall have ground-fault circuit-interrupter protection for personnel.

› All 125-volt, single-phase, 15-, 20-, and 30-amp outlets that are not part of the building's permanent wiring and are in use by personnel shall have GFCI protection for personnel.

» This applies to temporary wiring used during maintenance, remodeling, or repair of buildings, structures, or equipment or during similar construction-like activities.

» **Note**: A cord connector on an extension cord set is considered an outlet if the cord set is used for temporary electric power. Cord sets and devices with GFCI protection connected to the closest outlet are acceptable.

§1910.305(e), (f)

§1910.304(b)(3))

Standard for Health Care Facilities

When testing receptacle outlets, look for:

> physical integrity of outlet by visual inspection

> continuity of grounding circuit

> correct polarity

> 4 oz. or more of retention force of grounding blade, because if there is not enough retention force:

>> The cord and outlet gets hotter.

>> Arcing can occur among the plug and outlet.

>> An electrical fire may start.

>> There is potential for electrical shock.

Hazardous (Classified) Locations

Class I locations:

> are hazardous because flammable gases or vapors may produce explosive or ignitable mixtures.

Class II locations:

> are hazardous because of the presence of combustible dust.

Class III locations:

> are hazardous because of the presence of easily ignitable fibers or filings.

Safety STOP ™

OSHA Note — §1910.399

Easily ignitable fibers and filings include rayon, cotton (including cotton linters and cotton waste), sisal or henequen, istle, jute, hemp, tow, cocoa fiber, oakum, baled waste kapok, Spanish moss, wood chips, and other materials of similar nature.

Special Systems

Emergency circuit wiring intended to supply power for illumination and special loads in the event of failure of the normal supply must be kept independent of all other wiring and equipment and may not enter the same raceway, cable, box, or cabinet or other wiring, except:

> where common circuit elements suitable for the purpose are required; or

> for transferring power from the normal to the emergency source.

Where emergency lighting is necessary, the system must be so arranged that the failure of any individual lighting element, such as the burning out of a light bulb, will not leave any space in total darkness.

Training

Workers who face a risk of electric shock that is not reduced to a safe level by OSHA's electrical installation requirements must be trained in and be familiar with the electrical safety-related work practice requirements that apply to their job assignments.

In addition to these work practices, "qualified" persons (meaning those who are permitted to work on or near exposed energized parts because they have received training in and have demonstrated skills and knowledge in the construction and operation of electric equipment and installations and the hazards involved) must be trained in and be familiar with the following:

> how to distinguish exposed live parts from other parts of electric equipment

> how to determine nominal voltage of exposed live parts

> specified clearance distances and the corresponding voltages to which the qualified person will be exposed

> how to safely work on energized circuits

> the proper use of:

>> special precautionary techniques,

>> personal protective equipment,

§1910.308(b)(1)

§1910.308(b)(2)

§1910.332

§1910.331(a); §1910.332

§1910.332

» insulating and shielding materials, and

» insulated tools

Even if an electrical safety-related work practice is not specifically addressed by OSHA, "unqualified" employees (meaning those with little or no electrical training who work in the vicinity of energized electrical parts or could be affected by them) must be trained in and be familiar with such a practice if it is necessary for their safety.

The required training may be done either in a classroom or on the job. The degree of training necessary for each employee is determined by the risk to that employee.

Notes: Whether an employee is considered to be a "qualified person" will depend upon various circumstances in the workplace. It is possible, even likely, for an individual to be considered "qualified" with regard to certain equipment in the workplace, but "unqualified" as to other equipment.

Safety-Related Work Practices

De-energized Parts

Live parts to which an employee may be exposed shall be de-energized before the employee works on or near them, unless the employer can demonstrate that de-energizing introduces additional or increased hazards or is infeasible due to equipment design or operational limitations.

Energized Parts

When exposed live parts are not de-energized, use other safety-related work practices to protect employees who may be exposed to electrical hazards. These safety-related work practices are designed to protect employees against contact with energized circuit parts.

Work on Energized Equipment

Only qualified persons may work on electric circuit parts or equipment that has not been de-energized.

OSHA Note — §1910.333(a)

Working on or near exposed energized parts applies to work performed on exposed live parts (involving either direct contact or by means of tools or materials) or near enough to them for employees to be exposed to any hazard they present.

§1910.333(c)(3)(ii)

NIOSH Note

› As part of the NIOSH Fatality Assessment and Control Evaluation (FACE) program, 224 occupational electrocution incidents were investigated. They could have been prevented through compliance with existing OSHA, National Electric Code (NEC), and National Electrical Safety Code (NESC) regulations, and/or the use of adequate personal protective equipment (PPE).

› All workers should receive hazard awareness training so that they will be able to identify existing and potential hazards present in their workplaces and the potential serious injuries associated with them. Once these hazards are identified, employers should develop measures that would allow for their immediate control.

When a qualified person is working near overhead lines, whether in an elevated position or on the ground, the person may not approach or take any conductive object without an approved insulating handle closer to exposed energized parts than shown in Table S-5, unless:

› the person is insulated from the energized part;

» Gloves, with sleeves if necessary, rated for the voltage involved are considered to be insulation of the person from the energized part on which work is performed.

› the person is insulated from all conductive objects at a potential different from that of the energized part; and

› the energized part is insulated from the person and all other conductive objects at a different potential.

§1910.333(c) Table S-5

§1910.333(c)(3)(i)

§1910.333(c)(7)

§1910.333(c)(8)

Table S-5 - Approach Distances for Qualified Employees — Alternating Current	
Voltage range (phase to phase)	**Minimum approach distance**
300V and less	Avoid contact
Over 300V, not over 750V	1 ft. 0 in. (30.5 cm)
Over 750V, not over 2kV	1 ft. 6 in. (46 cm)
Over 2kV, not over 15kV	2 ft. 0 in. (61 cm)
Over 15kV, not over 37kV	3 ft. 0 in. (91 cm)
Over 37 kV, not over 87.5kV	3 ft. 6 in. (107 cm)
Over 87.5kV, not over 121kV	4 ft. 0 in. (122 cm)
Over 121kV, not over 140kV	4 ft. 6 in. (137 cm)

When an unqualified person is working in an elevated position near overhead lines or on the ground in the vicinity of overhead lines, neither the person nor the longest conductive object he or she may contact may come closer to any unguarded, energized overhead line than the following:

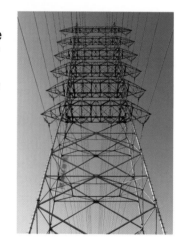

> Voltages to Ground 50kV or below: 10 feet

> Voltages to Ground over 50kV: 10 feet plus 4 inches for every 10kV over 50kV

Portable Ladders

Portable ladders shall have non-conductive siderails if they are used where the employee or the ladder could contact exposed energized parts.

Conductive Apparel

Conductive articles of jewelry and clothing such as watch bands, bracelets, rings, key chains, necklaces, metalized aprons, cloth with conductive thread, or metal headgear may not be worn if they might contact exposed energized parts.

Visual Inspection of Portable Electrical Equipment

Portable cord- and plug-connected equipment and flexible cord sets (extension cords) shall be visually inspected before use on any shift for:

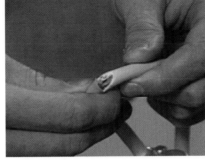

> external defects, such as loose parts, deformed and missing pins, or damage to outer jacket or insulation; and

> internal damage, such as pinched or crushed outer jacket.

If an inspection reveals a defect or damage that might expose an employee to injury, the defective or damaged item shall be removed from service. Employees may not use it until repairs and tests necessary to render the equipment safe have been made.

Employee's hands may not be wet when plugging and unplugging flexible cords and cord-and plug-connected equipment, if energized equipment is involved.

Personal Protective Equipment

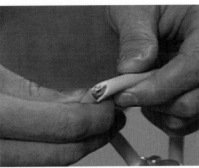

Use electrical protective equipment for the specific parts of the body to be protected and for the work to be performed.

Maintain PPE in a safe, reliable condition, and periodically inspect or test it.

Wear nonconductive head protection.

Wear eye and face protection wherever there is danger of injury to the eyes or face from electric arcs or flashes or from flying objects resulting from electrical explosion.

Alerting Techniques

The following alerting techniques shall be used to warn and protect employees from hazards:

> safety signs and tags

> barricades, where it is necessary to prevent or limit employee access to work areas

> attendants, if signs and barricades do not provide sufficient warning and protection from electrical hazards

§1910.334(a)(2)(i)

§1910.334(a)(2)(ii), (5)(i)

§1910.335(a)(1)

§1910.335(b)

Notes

Module Nineteen

Hazardous Waste Operations and Emergency Response

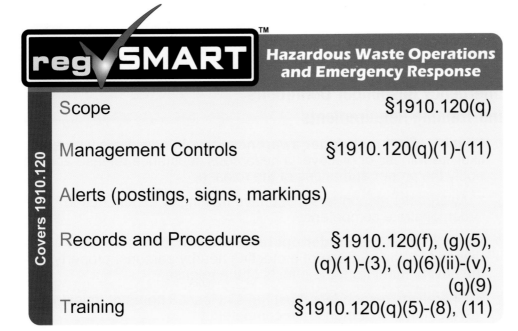

regSMART™	Hazardous Waste Operations and Emergency Response
Scope	§1910.120(q)
Management Controls	§1910.120(q)(1)-(11)
Alerts (postings, signs, markings)	
Records and Procedures	§1910.120(f), (g)(5), (q)(1)-(3), (q)(6)(ii)-(v), (q)(9)
Training	§1910.120(q)(5)-(8), (11)

Covers 1910.120

HAZWOPER

The Hazardous Waste Operations and Emergency Response (Hazwoper) Standard covers:

> clean-up operations;

> treatment, storage, and disposal facilities; and

> emergency response operations.

§1910.120(a)(1)

Emergency Response

Emergency Response Plan

A written emergency response plan shall be developed and implemented to handle anticipated emergencies prior to the commencement of emergency response operations.

§1910.120(q)(1)

Emergency Responder Definitions and Training Requirements

> **Level 1 - First responder awareness level:** Individuals who are likely to witness or discover a hazardous substance release and will notify the proper authorities of the release.

>> Awareness responders must have training or experience to demonstrate competency.

> **Level 2 - First responder operations level:** Individuals who respond for the purpose of protecting nearby persons, property, or the environment from the effects of the release.

>> Operations responders must have at least 8 hours of training or experience to demonstrate competency.

§1910.120(q)(6)(i)

> **Level 3 - Hazardous materials technician:** Individuals who respond to releases or potential releases for the purpose of stopping the release.

>> Technicians must have at least 24 hours of training equal to the first responder operations level and demonstrate additional competency.

§1910.120(q)(6)(ii)

§1910.120(q)(6)(iii)

> **Level 4 - Hazardous materials specialist:**
Individuals who respond with and provide support to hazardous materials technicians and have more direct or specific knowledge of the various substances.

>> Specialist must have at least 24 hours of training equal to the technician level and demonstrate additional competency.

> **Level 5 - On-site incident commander:**
Individuals who will assume control of the incident scene.

>> Incident commanders must have at least 24 hours of training equal to the first responder operations level and demonstrate additional competency.

§1910.120(q)(6)(iv)

§1910.120(q)(6)(v)

Documentation

Employers must certify the training and competency requirements have been met.

Training certification is required for levels 2, 3, 4, and 5.

Refresher Training

All levels of emergency response must have annual refresher training or demonstrate competency.

§1910.120(q)(6), (8)

Notes

Credits

Content for Prefix: Training Fundamentals
OSHA Training Guide, 15th Edition

Prefix - Training Fundamentals
hoover-5 by octal

Module 01: Intro to OSHA
CRSP. by ianmunroe

Module 02: RegLogic™
CGC Gallatin - Drydock by The MK Shop

Module 03: Walking-Working Surfaces
Not a step by Ano Lobb

Module 04: Exit Routes, Emergency Action Plans, and Fire Prevention Plans
Burrard Station Emergency Exit by sillygwailo
firealarm2a by jdurham
Get me out of the Stagecoach! by rightee
IMG_0612_w by xandert

Module 05: Fire Protection
DSCF1441 by ronnieb

Module 06: Electrical Cords
wires. by Jaako

Module 07: Recordkeeping, Part 1
PIC108543992297 by clarita

Module 08: Access to Employee Exposure and Medical Records
(SDSs)At National Prosthetics and Orthotics Boston by Nadya Peek
Paper files of medical records by Newtown grafitti

Module 09: Bloodborne Pathogens
wash by mensatic

Module 10: Hazard Communication, Part 1
(SDSs)At National Prosthetics and Orthotics Boston by Nadya Peek
CRSP. by ianmunroe
Europe District conducts construction safety class in Turkey by USACE Europe District
gasoline_and_water01 By ardelfin
HAZMAT 2.3 Poison Gas by SoulRider.222
Radiation Hazard by MountainAsh

Module 11: Inspections, Citations, and Penalties
(SDSs)At National Prosthetics and Orthotics Boston by Nadya Peek
Behind Bars by babukadja
Conference center receives USACE safety inspection by USACE Europe District
CRW_3536 by xandert
File Cabinets by grafixar
IMG00195 by | El Caganer
One_Hundred_Dollar_Bills_8654 (1) by alvimann
Paper files of medical records by Newtown grafitti

Module 12: Occupational Noise Exposure
Ear protection by Brett L.
Let the Sparks Fly - The Makita 2414NB Abrasive Cut Off Saw by toolshop

Module 13: Personal Protective Equipment
IMG00195 by | El Caganer
Let the Sparks Fly - Makita 9557NB Angle Grinder by toolstop

Module 14: Permit-Required Confined Spaces, Part 1
Brighton Sewer Tour by Dominic's pics
Certified Industrial Hygienist Dan Napier at Confined Space Site by MargaretNapier
confined space entry for installing flow monitoring equipment in the sewer at the combined sewer overflow point by Soggydan
confined space entry for installing flow monitoring equipment in the sewer at the combined sewer overflow point By Soggydan
Danger confined space by Pierre LaScott
Demineralized water storage tank by gogogadgetscott
img_2456 by mlinksva
img_2457 by mlinksva
SORS confined space by iraxmas
Storage tank cleaning by Marc Taylor
Untitled by Foxtongue

Module 15: Lockout/Tagout, Part 1
CGC Gallatin - Drydock by The MK Shop
hoover-5 by octal
Pueblo Chemical Agent-Destruction Pilot Plant Agent Filtration Area by Assembled Chemical Weapons Alternatives
tagged out by qnr
tag-in tag-out by a L p
Tag-out by Beige Alert

Module 16: Materials Handling and Storage
[2_365 | 02.01.2011] Working on Sunday? by MSVG
emergency shower_eye wash by peretzpup

Module 17: Machine Guarding
DSCN0639 by zabmo
Let the Sparks Fly - Makita 9557NB Angle Grinder by toolstop

Module 18: Electrical Requirements
energy_transfer by dave
fcien_75_ by Alvimann
gfci by Shifty
mf644 by jeltovski
PICT2395 by chelle
Power Line by dr_tr
Pylon by kayakaya
reset by samantha celera
tower crane by SoulRider.222
When Electricity Goes Bad by dbrulz123

Module 19: Hazardous Waste Operations and Emergency Response
HAZMAT exercise in Cobb County by Georgia National Guard
PHOTO Tradewinds 090308-M-8005L-TW01 by Exercise Tradewinds 2009
SUIT by post apocalyptic design
www.Army.mil by The U.S. Army

Notes

Index Vol I

H

Hand protection
    General requirements 114
Hazard assessment 109, 110
    Assessment guidelines 110
Hazard communication
    Application 76
    Combustible dust 78
    Container labeling 78, 79
    DOT HazMat labels 88
    Employee information and training 79
    Exceptions to labeling requirement 82
    Hazard communication program 78
    Hazard not otherwise classified 78
    Hazardous chemical, definition 77
    Hazard statement 80
    Health hazard 77
    List of hazardous chemicals 78
    Multi-employer workplaces 79
    Non-routine tasks 79
    Physical hazard 77
    Pictograms 80
    Precautionary statement 81
    Product identifier 79
    Purpose 76
    Pyrophoric gas 78
    regSMART 75
    Responsibility for container labeling 82
    Safety data sheets (SDSs) 78, 82
    Scope 76
    Sealed containers 78
    Signal word 80
    Simple asphyxiant 77
    Training 87
    Unlabeled pipes 79
Hazard Communications (HazCom)
    Hazardous chemicals list 78
    HazCom written program 78
    Labeling containers 79
Hazardous Chemical, definition 77
Hazardous waste operations and emergency response 185, 189
    Coverage of standard 186
    Emergency response plan 186
    regSMART 185, 189
    Responder, definitions 186
    Training 186, 187
    Training certification 187
Hazard statement (chemical), definition 80
Head protection 113
    General requirements 113
Health hazard (chemical), definition 77
Hearing loss, recording 53
Housekeeping
    Bloodborne pathogens 69

Housekeeping (continued)
    Bloodborne pathogens and laundry 71
    Materials handling and storage 152
    Walking-working surfaces 22

I

Illness (see also Injury)
    Definition 50
Imminent danger, definition 90
Injury
    Access to information 6
Injury (see also Illness)
    Commercial or public transportation 44
    Definition 50
    Fatality/hospitalization occuring long after incident 45
    Heart attack 45
    Motor vehicle accident 44
    Recordkeeping 45
    Reporting 44
Inspections
    Abrasive wheel machinery 165
    Flexible cords and cables 183
    Lockout/tagout 142
    Mechanical power presses 167
    OSHA (see Inspections, OSHA) 12
    Portable electrical equipment 183
    Powered industrial trucks 159
Inspections, Citations, and Penalties
    regSMART 89
Inspections, OSHA
    Appeals process 95
    Closing conference 94
    Employer rights 91
    Informal Conference 95
    Kit 91
    Notice of Contest 95
    Opening conference 92
    Preparation for 91
    Procedures 91
    Reasons for 90
    Review of records 93
    Walkaround inspection 93
    What to do if citation is issued 94
International Fire Code 30

L

Labeled, definition 42
Labels, hazard communication 79
Ladders 24
    Fall protection 25
    Mobile ladder stands 26
    Portable 182
    Safety and use 24